# A RESPONSORIAL PSALM BOOK

# A RESPONSORIAL PSALM BOOK

*The Responsorial Psalms from
the 3-year Lectionary Cycle
for Sundays and Feastdays*

Edited by Geoffrey Boulton Smith

*Settings by*
Robert Sherlaw Johnson
Laurence Bévenot
Stephen Dean
James Walsh
Christopher Walker
John Ainslie
Joseph Gelineau
Alan Rees
Paul Inwood
Martin Hall, etc.

**COLLINS**

Collins Liturgical Publications
8 Grafton Street, London W1X 3LA

Distributed in Ireland by
Educational Company of Ireland
21 Talbot Street, Dublin

Collins Liturgical Australia
PO Box 3023, Sydney 2001

Concordat cum originali: John P. Dewis 12 October 1979
Imprimatur: David Norris VG, Westminster 31 October 1979

ISBN 0 00 599638 4
First published 1980
Reprinted May 1985

Music origination by Collyer MacDonald London
Made and printed in Great Britain by
Bell and Bain Ltd., Glasgow

# CONTENTS

The principal aim of this book is to assist parishes to sing the Responsorial Psalms in the Lectionary for the Sundays and most important feasts of the three-year cycle. In selecting the contents the editor has borne in mind that resources are often limited, and has tried to include at least one setting for each Sunday that is simple to perform. Some parishes, however, prefer to use music that is a little more demanding, and so alternatives have also been provided for many Sundays.

There is need for variety in what is sung. Not only do the texts vary, and so require different treatment, but there is also a more general risk of monotony if all the music is of the same type. Thus the collection includes varied settings, some using simple psalm tones, others through-composed melody, by a considerable number of different composers, in the hope that the content will be enriched through variety of musical style. Whilst much of the music has been freshly written, and yet more appears in print for the first time, the collection has also drawn on previously published material by such composers as Gelineau, Bévenot and Murray, so that continuity may be preserved with the best of recent vernacular psalmody.

Another important consideration has been that what is sung in the liturgy should not only be readily performable, but also of good musical quality, and written in musical styles appropriate for contemporary worship. 'Composers, filled with the Christian spirit, should feel that their vocation is to cultivate sacred music and increase its store of treasures. Let them produce compositions which have the qualities proper to genuine sacred music, . . . providing also for the needs of small choirs and for the active participation of the entire assembly of the faithful' (Constitution on the Sacred Liturgy, n. 121). This collection has attempted, if only in a small way, to follow these high ideals.

Within the three-year cycle many psalms appear more than once. When this occurs, the musical settings have generally been used again, so that choirs and people may more rapidly become familiar with them. Even so, there is much fresh music to learn. This is so not only for the choir, which it is hoped will welcome the opportunity to sing something new, but also for the people, since each different response requires different music. Most of the responses, however, are simple, and, where they are short, can be picked up without rehearsal if sung through initially by the cantor or choir. Where the text is longer, and so requires more music, it is suggested that the congregation should be taken through the Response before the Mass begins.

In most of the psalms the verses may be sung either by a cantor or by the choir; if desired, the choir may be divided into two groups, singing alternate verses. The choir may also sometimes sing in harmony, though when this is possible in the responses, care should be taken that the congregation are sure of their melody; the people should never be encouraged simply to let the choir alone sing the response. (See also below, Practical Points, no. 8.)

Whilst individual settings of each psalm are included, it is not possible in a book of this size to do the same for every Alleluia verse and acclamation. Thus individual Alleluias are provided only for the most important feasts, but in addition there are many Alleluias that can be adapted to different texts.

The editor would like to thank all those who have contributed to this book, and especially the members of the Composers' Group of the Society of St Gregory. He would like to acknowledge his debt to the collection of psalms edited by Stephen Dean and published by the St Thomas More Centre for Pastoral Liturgy, from which a considerable number of settings have been taken. He would also like to thank John Ainslie for allowing him to use his analysis of the psalms in the Lectionary, and Paul Inwood for undertaking the copy-editing.

GEOFFREY BOULTON SMITH

# PRACTICAL POINTS

1.   There are two basic types of psalm-tone in this book:
    (a) reciting-note with cadence ('Bévenot type');
    (b) regularly-pulsed tone ('Gelineau type').

Apart from through-composed settings, there are a number of settings that do not conform completely to either main type; additionally there are a few 'mixed' settings with psalm-tones containing both Bévenot and Gelineau systems (e.g. the tones by Harold Barker).

2.   As far as possible, the notation used for each main type of tone has been standardised.

For the Bévenot type, the reciting-note is always a breve (𝄺), the final note of the cadence is always a minim (𝅗𝅥), and any notes immediately preceding the final note of the cadence are notated as quavers. In a few slightly more elaborate tones of this type, additional crotchets and/or semibreves may be found where the reciting-note is modified before the cadential formula is reached.

None of these note-values necessarily indicates the values that are actually to be sung; they are purely conventional, in the interests of making each main type of tone look the same and thus facilitating performance. For example, the duration of the final note of a cadence, relative to the preceding quavers, may well be shorter, or longer, than a minim, depending on the individual tone and the text itself. Nevertheless, this note will always be notated as a minim for the sake of uniformity.

In the Gelineau type of tone, the notation is simple and follows the customary style for this type. Reciting-notes are notated as semibreves (o), with additional notes as stemless crotchets (●). There are very few exceptions to this rule.

3.   Each main type of psalm-tone has its own system of pointing. Before going into details of the two systems, it should be said that with other types of tones the text is usually underlaid in full as if they were through-composed. Occasionally a more elaborate tone of one of the main types is also given a complete text-underlay where this makes it easier to understand how to fit text and music together.

4.   In the Bévenot type, the main pointing-symbol is the vertical stroke (|). This shows (a) where the reciting-note is quitted and (b) where the final note of the cadence is placed.

**Example**

Proclaim his | help day by | day,
tell among the nations | his | glory
and his wonders a|mong all the | peoples.

is sung as:

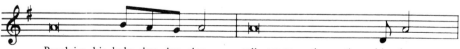

Proclaim his help day by day,     tell among the nations his glory

8

and his wonders a - mong all the peoples.

In tones (e.g. by Robert Sherlaw Johnson) where the reciting-note is itself preceded by one or two intonation-notes, an additional vertical stroke is used to remind the singer where the reciting-note starts in the line.

Example

when fitted with:     The word | of the | Lord is | faithful

or:     The Lord | looks on those | who re|vere him,

gives:

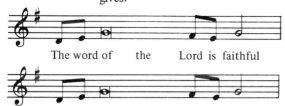

The word of     the     Lord is faithful

The Lord looks on those who re - vere him,

The most common form of Bévenot-type psalm-tone is that where the cadence-note is preceded by two quavers, and in the majority of cases the first of the two quavers coincides with the verbal accent. For example:

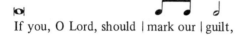

If you, O Lord, should | mark our | guilt,

However, there are many instances where the penultimate verbal accent comes not two but three syllables before the final accent, and many people tend to assume that the pointing is inaccurate in such cases. It is not, and a 'mental adjustment' is required when dealing with these cases. When faced with:

Many dogs | have sur|rounded me,
a band of the wick|ed be|set me.

it is important to follow the pointing given and *visualise:*

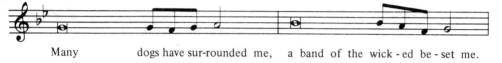

Many     dogs have sur-rounded me,     a band of the wick - ed be - set me.

The example above also makes another point. It would be less good to sing (though not a few do, ignoring the pointing and the sense of the words):

Many dogs have sur - round - ed me . . . . . .

An additional symbol is the decimal point (or 'blob'). This shows how text and music fit together where there are *more* syllables than notes in the cadence.

Example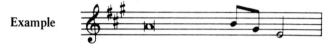

That is why I | love • your com|mands . . . .
Your will is | wonderful • in|deed;

The blobs show where to change note. These lines are therefore to be sung:

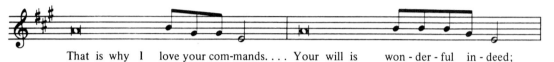

That is why I      love your com-mands. . . .  Your will is        won - der - ful   in - deed;

In cases where there are four syllables to only three notes, the following example will make it clear how to proceed:

Lift up the light of your | face on • us, O | Lord.

is sung as:

Lift up the light of your face on  us,  O   Lord.

A further symbol is the loop (‿) under the text, which shows how to fit text to music where there are *fewer* syllables than notes in the cadence. The loop coincides with a dotted slur over the relevant notes in the psalm-tone.

Example

I rejoiced when I | heard them | say:

is sung as:

I rejoiced when I  heard‿ them  say:

The loop is also very occasionally used to indicate words where two 'diphthongued' syllables should be sung more or less as one syllable to one note only (e.g. 'alien' — two syllables only). See also below under pronunciation.

5.    In the Gelineau type of psalm-tone, the principal pointing-symbol is the acute accent (´). The accent always coincides with a new semibreve in the tone.

Example

O give the Lórd, you sóns of Gód,

is sung as:

O give the Lord, you sons of God,

The 'blob' is also occasionally used with Gelineau-type tones where there are subsidiary notes (stemless crotchets) between two semibreves and where the number of syllables to be fitted in does not correspond.

Example

He does not tréat us • accórding • to our síns

is sung as:

He does not treat us ac - cording to our sins

In rare instances the loop will be found in conjunction with Gelineau-type tones in cases where more than one subsidiary note has to be sung to the same syllable.

Example

slow to ánger and rích in mércy.

is sung as:

slow to anger and rich in mercy

The slur over (or under) notes (e.g. ⌢⌣ ) in Gelineau-type tones merely serves to indicate the part-writing in cases which might otherwise (because of the lack of stems) be ambiguous. It has no other significance whatsoever.

6. In a number of cases a psalm will be associated with two simple tones, one Bévenot-type and one Gelineau-type. In such cases the text will carry both systems of pointing simultaneously. This will cause no problems in practice. On the rare occasions where one of the two symbols common to both systems — blob or loop — is found, it will be clear from inspection of the tones which tone the symbol applies to.

In one or two isolated instances a 'Gelineau blob' occurs in the same place as a Bévenot vertical stroke. In such instances the blob is omitted, the vertical stroke doing duty for both symbols.

The rúle of the Lórd is | to be | trústed,

will mean, in practice:    The rule of the Lord is | to be | trusted,
                           The rúle of the Lórd is • to be trústed,     and will be sung:

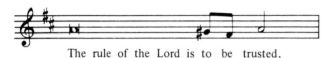

The rule of the Lord is to be trusted,

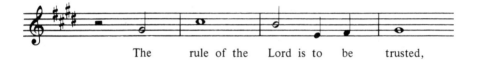

The           rule of the      Lord is to       be        trusted,

7.    In the few cases of 'mixed' tones (see section 1, above), each line of text is pointed according to the system used in the corresponding line of music.

8.    A number of the Responses may be sung by SATB choir in parts, even though this is not indicated. A number of others can also be sung in this way if the note-values in the under-parts are subdivided to fit the syllables. It is recommended that the choir should not sing the Response in parts until the melody-line has been properly assimilated by the people.
It is important to remember, however, that there is a lot of difference in terms of *sound* between a single cantor singing a psalm-verse and a group of men or women doing the same thing in unison (or, with a mixed choir, in octaves). Some composers will have conceived their music in terms of a cantor rather than a choir; and if the music sounds a little strange when performed by a choir it is best to revert, where possible, to one or two cantors only.
Guitar-chords have been provided for a number of items. Attention is drawn to the capo instructions where given. Where guitar-chords should not be used simultaneously with the keyboard accompaniment provided, this is noted in a rubric.

9.    With very rare exceptions (occurring only in Responses), words such as *heaven* and *power* should be pronounced as one syllable only, and words such as *Israel, prisoner* and *glorious* as two syllables only, even though none of these is printed with an apostrophe. The loop (see above) is sometimes used as a reminder of this.

10.    With each setting, it is to be assumed that the first composer mentioned has also composed all the remaining music in that setting unless otherwise specified.

# 1ST SUNDAY OF ADVENT, YEAR A
## Christ the King, Year C
## Dedication of a Church

**Response**      DENIS McCARTHY

**Psalm-Tone**      LAURENCE BÉVENOT

**Ps 121**

1.   I rejoiced when I | heard them | say:
   'Let us go to | God's | house.'
   And now our feet | are | standing
   within your | gates, O Je|rusalem.   ℟.

2.   Jerusalem is | built as a | city
   strongly | com|pact.
   It is there that the tribes | go | up,
   the | tribes of the | Lord.   ℟.

| *1 Advent A* | *Christ the King C* |
|---|---|
| 3.   For love of my \| bre\|thren and \| friends<br>I say: 'Peace \| up\|on\|you!'<br>For love of the house of \| the \| Lord<br>I will \| ask for your \| good.   ℟. | 3.   For Israel's \| law it \| is,<br>there to praise \| the \| Lord's name.<br>There were set the thrones \| of \| judgement<br>of the \| house of \| David.   ℟. |

*For the Dedication of a Church, sing all the verses given here - see Lectionary.*

# 2ND SUNDAY OF ADVENT, YEAR A

**Response**                                                     JAMES WALSH

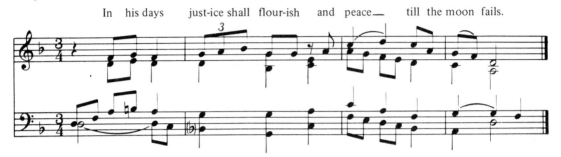

In his days  just-ice shall flour-ish  and peace___  till the moon fails.

**Psalm-Tone**

**Ps 71**

1. O God, give your judgement to the | king,
   to a king's son your | justice,
   that he may judge your peo|ple in | justice
   and your poor | in right | judgement.   ℟.

2. In his days justice shall | flourish
   and peace till the | moon fails.
   He shall rule from | sea to | sea,
   from the Great River to | earth's | bounds.   ℟.

3. For he shall save the poor when they | cry
   and the needy who are | helpless.
   He will have pity | on the | weak
   and save the lives | of the | poor.   ℟.

4. May his name be blessed for | ever
   and endure like the | sun.
   Every tribe shall be | blessed in | him,
   all nations | bless his | name.   ℟.

# 3RD SUNDAY OF ADVENT, YEAR A
## 4th Sunday of the Year, Year A

### 1ST SETTING

**Response, 3 Advent A**      ALAN REES

**Response, 4 Year A**

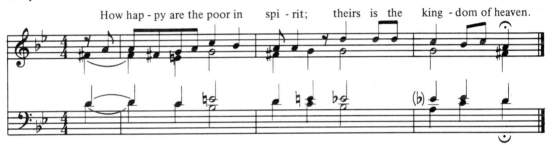

**Psalm-Tone**      LAURENCE BÉVENOT

**Ps 145**

1.    It is he who keeps | faith for | ever,
   who is just to those who | are op|pressed.
   It is he who gives bread | to the | hungry,
   the Lord, who sets | prisoners | free. ℟.

2.    *The Lord who gives sight | to the | blind,
   who raises up those who | are bowed | down,
   the Lord, who pro|tects the | stranger
   and upholds the wi|dow and | orphan. ℟.

3.    It is the Lord who | loves the | just
   but thwarts the path | of the | wicked.
   The Lord will | reign for | ever,
   Zion's God, from | age to | age. ℟.

*On the 4th Sunday of Year A, this verse begins 'It is the Lord . . .'.*

*An alternative setting will be found on p. 71.*

## 2ND SETTING

Response, 3 Advent A                                    GEOFFREY BOULTON SMITH

* *Sung by a semi-chorus. When the response is sung twice (at the beginning) the whole choir sings the people's part the first time.*

Alternative response, 3 Advent A and 4 Year A

* *See note above.*

**Psalm 145**

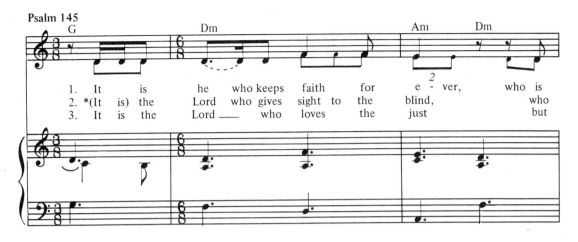

1. It is he who keeps faith for e - ver, who is
2. *(It is) the Lord who gives sight to the blind, who
3. It is the Lord ___ who loves the just but

* 4 Year A only

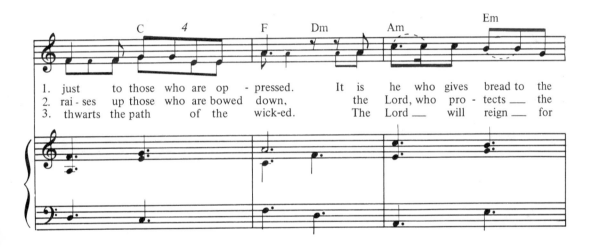

1. just to those who are op - pressed. It is he who gives bread to the
2. rai - ses up those who are bowed down, the Lord, who pro - tects ___ the
3. thwarts the path of the wick-ed. The Lord ___ will reign ___ for

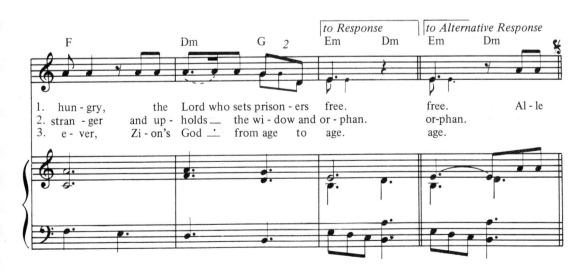

to Response | to Alternative Response

1. hun - gry, the Lord who sets prison - ers free. free. Al - le
2. stran - ger and up - holds ___ the wi - dow and or - phan. or-phan.
3. e - ver, Zi - on's God ___ from age to age. age.

# 4TH SUNDAY OF ADVENT, YEAR A
## All Saints, Years A, B and C

**Response, 4 Advent A**

ALAN REES

Let the Lord en - ter! He is the king of glo - ry.

**Response, All Saints**

Such are the men who seek your face, O Lord.

**Psalm-Tone**

**Ps 23**

1. The Lord's is the | earth and • its | fullness,
   the world and | all its | peoples.
   It is he who set it | on the | seas;
   on the waters he | made it | firm.   ℟.

2. Who shall climb the | mountain of • the | Lord?
   Who shall stand in his | holy | place?
   The man with clean hands | and pure | heart,
   who desires not | worthless | things.   ℟.

3. He shall receive | blessings from • the | Lord
   and reward from the | God who | saves him.
   Such are the | men who | seek him,
   seek the face of the | God of | Jacob.   ℟.

# CHRISTMAS: MIDNIGHT MASS

**Response**                                                                 LAURENCE BÉVENOT

**Response**, alternative harmonisation                                       (G.B.S.)

**Psalm-Tone**                                     Omit v.4                   LAURENCE BÉVENOT

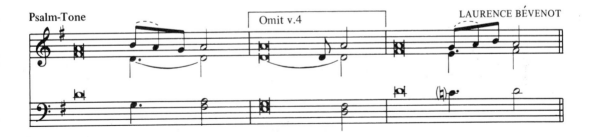

**Ps 95**

1.  O sing a new | song to the | Lord,
    sing to the Lord all | the | earth.
    O sing to the | Lord, bless his | name.   ℟.

2.  Proclaim his | help day by | day,
    tell among the nations | his | glory
    and his wonders a|mong all the | peoples.   ℟.

3.  Let the heavens rejoice and | earth be | glad,
    let the sea and all within it thun¦der | praise,
    let the land and all it | bears re|joice,
        *(repeat whole psalm-tone)*
    all the trees of the | wood shout for | joy
    at the presence of the Lord for | he | comes,
    he comes to | rule the | earth.   ℟.

4.  With justice he will | rule the world,
    he will judge the | peoples • with his | truth.   ℟.

# CHRISTMAS: DAY MASS
## 6th Sunday of Easter, Year B
## 28th Sunday of the Year, Year C

**Response, Christmas Day**                              GEOFFREY BOULTON SMITH

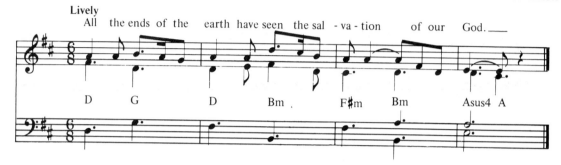

**Response, 6 Easter B and 28 Year C**

**Alternative Response, 6 Easter B**

Psalm 97

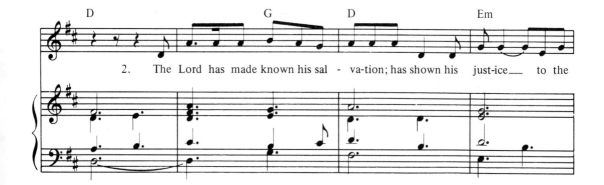

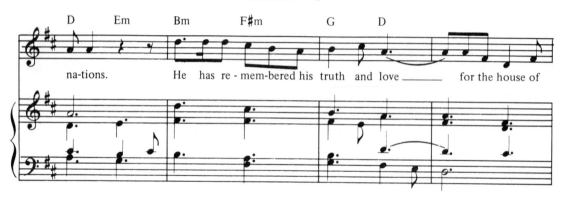

na-tions. He has re - mem-bered his truth and love _____ for the house of

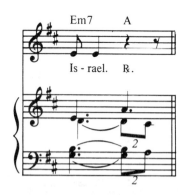

Is - rael. ℞.

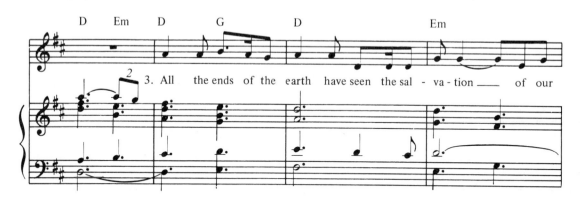

3. All the ends of the earth have seen the sal - va - tion _____ of our

God. Shout to the Lord all the earth, ring out, _____ ring out your

*Christmas Day only*

4. Sing psalms to the Lord with the harp, with the sound of music. With trum-pets and the sound of the horn ac-claim the

King, the Lord. ℟.

*An alternative setting will be found on p.120.*

# HOLY FAMILY
## 33rd Sunday of the Year, Year A

**Response, Holy Family**                      1st SETTING                      PAUL INWOOD

**Response, 33 Year A**

**Psalm-Tone**

**Ps 127**

1.  O blessed are those who | fear the | Lord
    and | walk in his | ways!
    By the labour of your hands | you shall | eat.
    You will be | happy and | prosper.   R.

2.  Your wife like a | fruitful | vine
    in the | heart of your | house;
    your children like | shoots of • the | olive
    a|round your | table.   R.

*Holy Family*

3.  Indeed | thus shall • be | blessed
    the man who | fears the | Lord.
    May the Lord | bless you • from | Zion
    all the | days of your | life.   R.

*33 Year A*

3.  Indeed | thus shall • be | blessed
    the man who | fears the | Lord.
    May the Lord | bless you • from | Zion
    in a happy Jerusalem all the | days of your | life.   R.

**Response, Holy Family**  2nd SETTING  PAUL JOHNSTONE

O bless-ed are those who fear the Lord and walk in——

—— his ways.

**Response, 33 Year A**

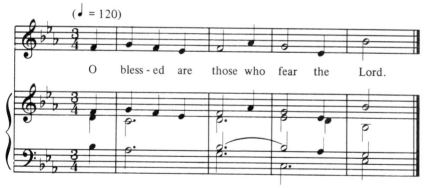

O bless-ed are those who fear the Lord.

Psalm 127

*Verses 1 and 2 (both days)*

1. O bless - ed are those who fear ___ the Lord and walk in his
2. Your wife like a fruit - ful vine in the heart of your

Omit v. 2

Omit v. 2

1. ways! ___ By the la - bour of your hands you shall eat. You will be
2. house; ___ your ___ child - ren like shoots of the o - live a -

1. hap - py and pros - per. ℞.
2. -round your ta - ble. ℞.

*Verse 3, Holy Family*

In - deed - thus shall be bless - ed the man ___ who

fears the Lord._____ May the Lord bless you from Zi -

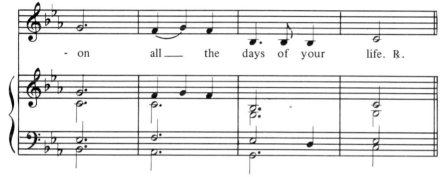

- on all ___ the days of your life. R.

*Verse 3, 33 Year A*

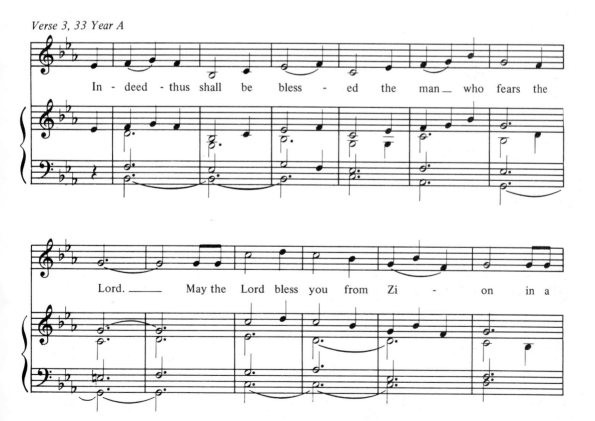

In - deed - thus shall be bless - ed the man _ who fears the

Lord. _____ May the Lord bless you from Zi - on in a

hap - py Je - ru - sa - lem all ___ the

days of your life. ℟.

## 2ND SUNDAY AFTER CHRISTMAS
### Corpus Christi, Year A

**Response, 2nd after Christmas**      GEOFFREY BOULTON SMITH

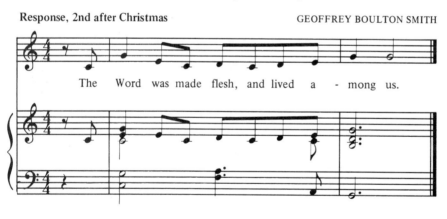

The Word was made flesh, and lived a - mong us.

**Response, Corpus Christi Year A**

Choir (optional)

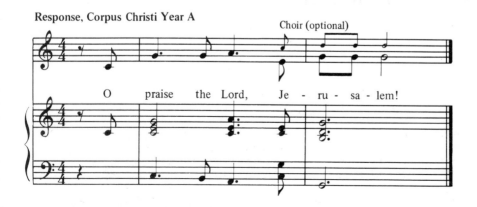

O praise the Lord, Je - ru - sa - lem!

**Alternative Response, 2nd after Christmas and Corpus Christi**

Al - le - lu - ia, al - le - lu - ia!

**Psalm-Tone**

v. 3 only

Al - le - lu - ia!

v. 3 only

**Ps 147**

1. O práise the Lórd, Jerúsalem!
   Zíon, práise your Gód!
   He has stréngthened the bárs of your gátes,
   he has bléssed the children • withín you.  ℟.

2. He estáblished péace • on your bórders,
   he féeds you with fínest whéat.
   He sénds out his wórd to the éarth
   and swíftly rúns • his commánd.  ℟.

3. He mákes his word knówn to Jácob,
   to Ísrael his láws • and decrées.
   He has not déalt thus with óther nátions;
   he has not táught them hís decrées.
   Alleluia!  ℟.

## January 6
## EPIPHANY

**Response**                                                    JAMES WALSH

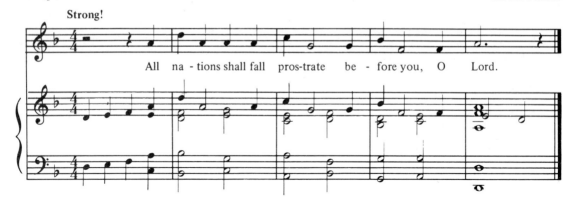

All na - tions shall fall pros-trate be - fore you, O Lord.

**Psalm-Tone**

**Ps 71**

1. O God, give your judgement to | the | king,
   to a king's | son your | justice,
   that he may judge your | people • in | justice
   and your poor | in right | judgement.   ℞.

2. In his days justice | shall | flourish
   and peace | till the • moon | fails.
   He shall rule from | sea to | sea,
   from the Great River | to earth's | bounds.   ℞.

3. The kings of Tarshish and the sea coasts shall
                            pay | him | tribute.
   The kings of Sheba and Seba shall | bring him
                                       | gifts.
   Before him all kings | shall fall | prostrate,
   all na|tions shall | serve him.   ℞.

4. For he shall save the poor when | they | cry
   and the needy | who are | helpless.
   He will have pity | on the | weak
   and save the lives | of the | poor.   ℞.

## Sunday after Epiphany
## FEAST OF THE BAPTISM OF OUR LORD
### 1ST SETTING

**Response**                    DENIS McCARTHY

The Lord will bless his peop - le with peace.

**Psalm-Tone**

LAURENCE BÉVENOT

Ps 28

1. O give the Lórd you | sóns of | Gód,
   give the Lórd gló|ry and | pówer;
   give the Lórd the glóry | of his | náme.
   Adore the Lórd in his | hóly | cóurt.  ℞.

2. The Lórd's voice resóunding | on the | wáters,
   the Lórd on the imménsi|ty of | wáters;
   the vóice of the Lórd, | full of | pówer,
   the vóice of the Lórd, | full of | spléndour.  ℞.

3. The Gód of | glóry | thúnders.
   In his témple they | áll cry: | 'Glóry!'
   The Lórd sat enthróned o|ver the | flóod;
   the Lórd sits as | kíng for | éver.  ℞.

## 2nd SETTING

**Response**

A. GREGORY MURRAY

The Lord will bless his peo-ple with peace.

**Psalm-Tone**

JOSEPH GELINEAU

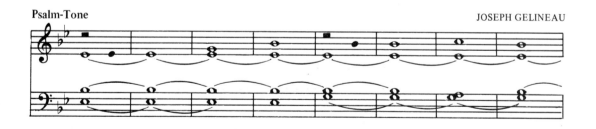

# 1ST SUNDAY OF LENT, YEAR A
## 24th Sunday of the Year, Year C
## Ash Wednesday
### 1st SETTING

**Response, 1 Lent A**                 GEOFFREY BOULTON SMITH

Have mer-cy on us, O  Lord,  for  we  have sinned.

**Response, 24 Year C**

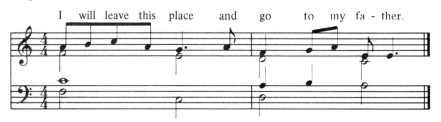

I  will  leave  this  place    and    go    to    my  fa - ther.

**Psalm-Tone**                                              JOSEPH GELINEAU

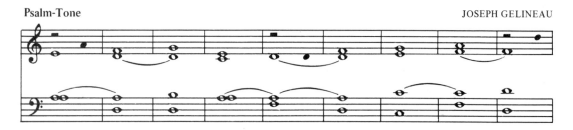

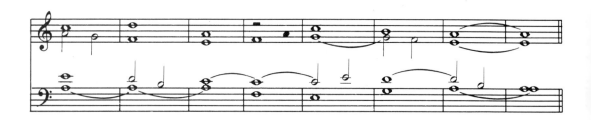

**Ps 50**

1.  Have mércy on me, Gód, in your kíndness.
    In your compássion blot óut my offénce.
    O wásh me more and móre from my gúilt
    and cléanse me fróm my sín.   R.

1a.  *(1 Lent A only)*
    My offénces trúly I knów them;
    my sín is álways befóre me.
    Against yóu, you alóne, have I sínned;
    what is évil in your síght • I have dóne.   R.

2. A púre heart creáte for me, O Gód,
   put a stéadfast spírit withín me.
   Do not cást me awáy from your présence,
   nor depríve me of your hóly spírit.  ℞.

3. *(1 Lent A only)*
   Give me agáin the jóy of your hélp;
   with a spírit of férvour sustáin me.
   O Lórd, ópen my líps
   and my móuth shall decláre your práise.  ℞.

3. *(24 Year C only)*
   O Lórd, ópen my líps
   and my móuth shall decláre your práise.
   My sácrifice is a cóntrite spírit;
   a húmbled, contrite héart you • will not spúrn.  ℞.

*For Ash Wednesday the Response and verses are as for 1 Lent A.*

2nd SETTING

**Response, 1 Lent A**                                   TONY BARR

Have mer-cy on us, O Lord, for  we have sinned.

**Response, 24 Year C**

I  will leave   this place and go  to  my Father.

**Psalm-Tone**

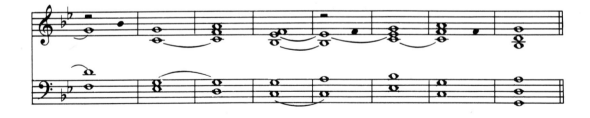

# 2ND SUNDAY OF LENT, YEAR A
## Trinity Sunday, Year B
### 29th Sunday of the Year, Year B
#### 1st SETTING

**Response, 2 Lent A, 29 Year B**                     ROBERT SHERLAW JOHNSON

May your love be up-on us, O Lord,__ as we place all our hope in you.

**Response, Trinity B**

Hap-py the peo-ple the Lord has chos-en as his own.

**Psalm-Tone**

Ps 32

1.  *The wórd | of the | Lórd is | fáithful
    and áll his wórks | to be | trústed.
    The Lórd loves | jústice • and | right
    and fílls the | éarth with his | lóve.  ℞.

1a. *(Trinity B only)*
    By his | wórd the | héavens were | máde,
    by the bréath of his móuth | all the | stárs.
    He spoke, and they | cáme to | bé.
    He commánded; they | spráng into | béing.  ℞.

*On the 2nd Sunday of Lent, Year A, the* Lectionary *erroneously begins v. 1 with the word 'For'.*

2. The Lórd | looks on thóse | who re|vére him,
   on thóse who hópe | in his | lóve,
   to réscue their | sóuls from | déath,
   to kéep them allíve in | fámine.   ℞.

3. Our sóul | is wáiting | for the | Lórd.
   The Lórd is our hélp | and our | shíeld.
   May your lóve be up|ón us, • O | Lórd,
   as we pláce all our | hópe in | yóu.   ℞.

## 2nd SETTING

Response, 2 Lent A                                    BILL TAMBLYN

Psalm-Tone                                         JOSEPH GELINEAU

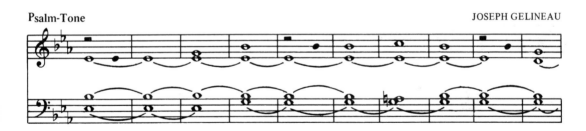

## 3RD SUNDAY OF LENT, YEAR A

23rd Sunday of the Year, Year A　　18th Sunday of the Year, Year C
4th Sunday of the Year, Year B　　27th Sunday of the Year, Year C

**Response**　　　　　　　　　1st SETTING　　　　ROBERT SHERLAW JOHNSON

O that to-day you would lis-ten to his voice! Har-den not your hearts.

**Psalm-Tone**　　　　　　　　Omit v. 1

**Ps 94**

1. Come, ring | out our joy to | the | Lord;
   hail the | rock who | saves us.
   Let us come before him, | giving | thanks,
   with songs | let us hail the | Lord. ℟.

2. Come in; | let us bow and | bend | low;
   let us kneel before the | God who | made us
   for he is our | God and | we
   the people who belong | to his | pasture,
   the flock | that is led by • his | hand. ℟.

3. O that | today you would listen to | his | voice!
   'Harden not your hearts as | at Me|ribah,
   as on that day at Massah | in the | desert
   when your fathers put me | to the | test;
   when they tried me, | though they saw my | work.' ℟.

**Response**　　　　　　　　　2nd SETTING　　　　　JAMES WALSH

O that to-day you would lis-ten to his voice! Har-den not your hearts.

**Psalm-Tone**

Ps 94

1. Come, ring out our joy | to the | Lord;
   hail the | rock who | saves us.
   Let us come before him, | giving | thanks,
   with songs let us | hail the | Lord.  ℟.

2. Come in; let us bow | and bend | low;
   let us kneel before the | God who | made us
   for he is our God and we the people who
   belong | to his | pasture,
   the flock that is led | by his | hand.  ℟.

3. O that today you would listen | to his | voice!
   'Harden not your hearts as at Meribah, as on
   that day at Massah | in the | desert
   when your fathers put me | to the | test;
   when they tried me, though they | saw my |
   work.'  ℟.

Response                    3rd SETTING                    GEOFFREY BOULTON SMITH

Psalm 94

**Poco più mosso**

2. Come in; let us bow and bend low; let us kneel be - fore the God who

made us for he is our God and we the peo-ple who be - long to his

pas-ture, the flock that is led by his hand. ℟.

**Poco più mosso**

3. O that to - day you would lis - ten to his voice! 'Har-den not your hearts as at Me -

-ri - bah,       as   on that day   at   Mas - sah   in   the   des - ert   when your

fa - thers put me to the   test;      when they tried    me, though they saw my work.'   ℞.

**Optional alternative harmonisations** *(a) for final Response, (b) for SATB Response*

*(a)*     O   that   to - day you would    lis - ten to his voice!      Har-den not your    hearts.

*(b)*     O   that    to - day    you would lis - ten   to   his voice!       Har-den not     your   hearts.

you would

Har-den   not    your hearts, not your

# 4TH SUNDAY OF LENT, YEAR A
## 4th Sunday of Easter, Year A
## 28th Sunday of the Year, Year A
## 16th Sunday of the Year, Year B
### 1st SETTING

**Response, 4 Lent A, 4 Easter A, 16 Year B**

A. GREGORY MURRAY

The Lord is my shep - herd; there is no-thing I shall want.

**Response, 28 Year A**

GEOFFREY BOULTON SMITH

In the Lord's own house shall I dwell for e - ver and e - ver.

**Psalm 22**

JOSEPH GELINEAU

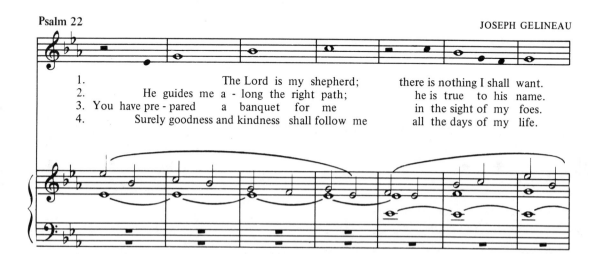

1. The Lord is my shepherd; there is nothing I shall want.
2. He guides me a - long the right path; he is true to his name.
3. You have pre - pared a banquet for me in the sight of my foes.
4. Surely goodness and kindness shall follow me all the days of my life.

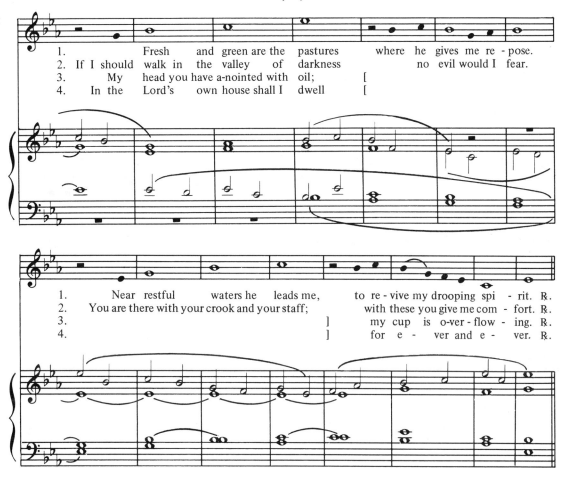

1. Fresh and green are the pastures where he gives me re-pose.
2. If I should walk in the valley of darkness no evil would I fear.
3. My head you have a-nointed with oil; [
4. In the Lord's own house shall I dwell [

1. Near restful waters he leads me, to re-vive my drooping spi - rit. ℞.
2. You are there with your crook and your staff; with these you give me com - fort. ℞.
3. ] my cup is o-ver-flow - ing. ℞.
4. ] for e - ver and e - ver. ℞.

2nd SETTING

**Response, 4 Lent A, 4 Easter A, 16 Year B**　　　CHRISTOPHER McCURRY

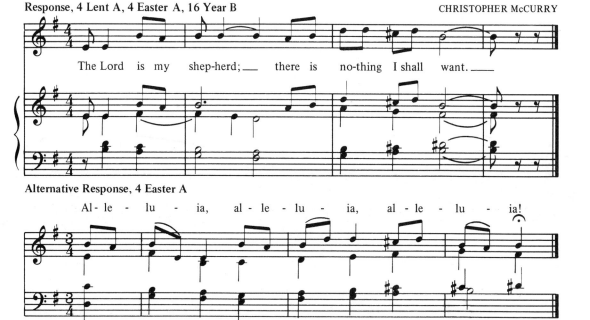

The Lord is my shep-herd;__ there is no-thing I shall want.__

**Alternative Response, 4 Easter A**

Al - le - lu - ia, al - le - lu - ia, al - le - lu - ia!

**Response, 28 Year A**

In the Lord's own house shall I dwell for e - ver and e - ver.

**Psalm 22**

1. The Lord is my shepherd; there is nothing I shall want.
2. He guides me a - long the right path; ____ he is true to his name. ____
*(Steady beat - à la Gelineau)*

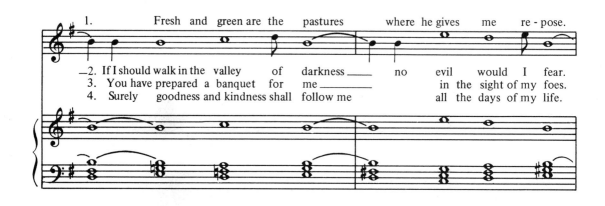

1. Fresh and green are the pastures where he gives me re - pose.

—2. If I should walk in the valley of darkness ____ no evil would I fear.
3. You have prepared a banquet for me ____ in the sight of my foes.
4. Surely goodness and kindness shall follow me all the days of my life.

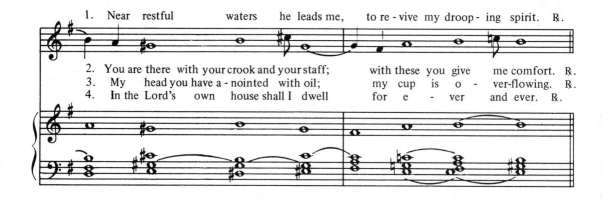

1. Near restful waters he leads me, to re - vive my droop - ing spirit. ℟.

2. You are there with your crook and your staff; with these you give me comfort. ℟.
3. My head you have a - nointed with oil; my cup is o - ver-flowing. ℟.
4. In the Lord's own house shall I dwell for e - ver and ever. ℟.

# 5TH SUNDAY OF LENT, YEAR A
## 10th Sunday of the Year, Year B

**Response**                                   1st SETTING                                   PETER SMEDLEY

**Ps 129**

1. Out of the dépths I crý to | you, O | Lórd,
Lórd, | hear my | vóice!
O lét your éars be at|tént|ive
to the vóice | of my | pléading.  ℟.

2. If you, O Lórd, should | márk our | gúilt,
Lórd, who | would sur|víve?
But with yóu is fóund for|gíve|ness:
for thís | we re|vére yóu.  ℟.

*3. My sóul is wáiting | for the | Lórd,
I cóunt | on his | wórd.
My sóul is lónging for | the | Lórd
more than wátch|man for | dáybréak.  ℟.

4. Becáuse with the Lórd | there is | mércy
and fúllness | of re|démption,
Ísrael indéed he will | re|déem
from áll | its i|níquitý.  ℟.

*\*The Lectionary for 5 Lent A  erroneously gives two additional lines at the end of this verse.*

**Response**                           2nd SETTING                           GEOFFREY BOULTON SMITH

**Psalm-Tone**                                                                    JOSEPH GELINEAU

## PASSION SUNDAY
### (Palm Sunday)

Response                           1st SETTING                          STEPHEN DEAN

My God, my God, why have you for - sa - ken me?

Psalm 21

1. All who see me                de - ride me.        They curl their lips, they    toss their
2. Many dogs have                sur-rounded me,      a band of the wick - ed      be -
3. They divide my clothing       a - mong them.       They cast lots               for my
4. I will tell your name to      my brethren          and praise you where they are   as -

1. heads.    'He  trusted in the                              Lord,    let   him
2. -set me.  They  tear holes in my                           hands    and   my
3. robe.     O   Lord, do not                                 leave    me   a -
4. -sembled. [  ] 'You who fear the Lord, give him praise; all sons of Jacob, give  him

1. save him;   let him re - lease him if this  is   his  friend.'  ℟.
2. feet.     I    can count every one of  my   bones.  ℟.
3. - lone,   [ ]  my strength, make  haste to   help me.  ℟.
4. glory.    [ ]  Re - vere him,     Is - rael's  sons.'  ℟.

## 2nd SETTING

**Response**                                             JOHN AINSLIE

My God, my God,        why have you for - sa - ken    me?

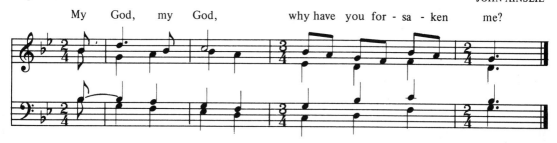

**Psalm-Tone**

**Ps 21**

1. All who see | me de|ride me.
   They curl their lips, they | toss their | heads.
   'He trusted in the Lord, | let him | save him;
   let him release him if this | is his | friend.'  ℞.

2. Many dogs | have sur|rounded me,
   a band of the wick|ed be|set me.
   They tear holes in my hands | and my | feet.
   I can count every one | of my | bones.  ℞.

3. They divide my cloth|ing a|mong them.
   They cast lots | for my | robe.
   O Lord, do not leave | me a|lone,
   my strength, make | haste to | help me.  ℞.

4. I will tell of your name | to my | brethren
   and praise you where they | are as|sembled.
   'You who fear the Lord, give him praise; all
                    sons of Jacob | give him | glory.
   Revere him, | Israel's | sons.'  ℞.

# MAUNDY THURSDAY
## Evening Mass

**Response**

STEPHEN DEAN

The bless - ing-cup that we bless is a com-mun - ion with the blood of Christ.

**Psalm 115**

1. How can I re - pay the Lord    for his    good - ness to me?
2. O precious in the eyes of the Lord    is the    death of his faithful.
3. A thanksgiving sacri - fice I make:    I will call on the Lord's name.

1. The cup of sal - va - tion I will raise;    I will call on the Lord's name. ℟.
2. Your servant, Lord, your ser - vant am I;    you have loosened my bonds. ℟.
3. My vows to the Lord I will ful - fil    be - fore all his people. ℟.

**Gospel Acclamation**

STEPHEN DEAN, adapted G.B.S.

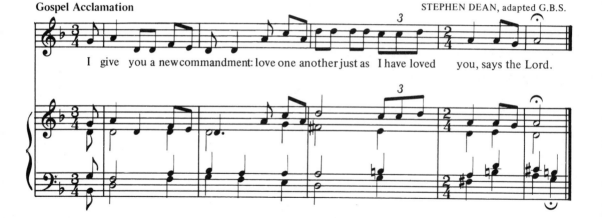

I give you a new commandment: love one another just as I have loved you, says the Lord.

# GOOD FRIDAY

**Response**                                            PLAINCHANT, arr. G.B.S.

Fa - ther, in - to your hands   I com-mend my— spi - rit.

**Psalm-Tone**                                  GEOFFREY BOULTON SMITH

Ps 30

1. In you, O Lord, | I take | refuge.
   Let me never be | put to | shame.
   In your justice set me free. Into your hands I com|mend my | spirit.
   It is you who will re|deem me, | Lord.   ℟.

2. In the face of | all my | foes
   I am | a re|proach,
   an object of scorn | to my | neighbours
   and of fear | to my | friends.   ℟.

3. Those who see me | in the | street
   run far a|way from | me.
   I am like a dead man, forgotten | in men's | hearts,
   like a thing | thrown a|way.   ℟.

4. But as for me, I | trust in • you, | Lord,
   I say: 'You | are my | God.'
   My life is in your | hands, de|liver me
   from the hands of | those who | hate me.   ℟.

5. Let your face shine | on your | servant,
   Save me | in your | love.
   Be strong, let your | heart take | courage,
   all who hope | in the | Lord.   ℟.

# EASTER VIGIL, 1ST PSALM
*See Pentecost, p.65.*

# EASTER VIGIL, 1ST PSALM, alternative
*See 7th Sunday of the Year, Year A, first two settings, p.73.*

# EASTER VIGIL, 2ND PSALM
*See 33rd Sunday of the Year, Year B, p.150.*

# EASTER VIGIL, 3RD PSALM

**Response**     1st SETTING     BILL TAMBLYN

2nd SETTING

GEOFFREY BOULTON SMITH

LAURENCE BÉVENOT

**Ex 15**

1. I will sing to the Lord, | glorious his | triumph!
   Horse and rider he has thrown in|to the | sea!
   The Lord is my strength, my song, | my sal|vation.
   This is my God and | I ex|tol him.
   my fathers' God and I | give him | praise.  ℞.

2. The Lord is a warrior! The | Lord is his | name.
   The chariots of Pharaoh he hurled in|to the | sea,
   the flower of his army is drowned | in the | sea.
   The deeps hide them; they | sank like a | stone.  ℞.

3. Your right hand, Lord, | glorious • in its | power,
   your right hand, Lord, has shat|tered the | enemy.
   In the greatness of your glory you | crushed the | foe.  ℞.

4. You will lead them and | plant them • on your | mountain,
   the place, O Lord, where you have | made your | home,
   the sanctuary, Lord, which your | hands have | made.
   The Lord will reign for | ever and | ever.  ℞.

# EASTER VIGIL, 4TH PSALM
*See 13th Sunday of the Year, Year B, p.132.*

# EASTER VIGIL, 5TH PSALM
*See 3rd Sunday of Advent, Year C, p.153.*

# EASTER VIGIL, 6TH PSALM
*See 3rd Sunday of Lent, Year B, p.112.*

# EASTER VIGIL, 7TH PSALM

**Psalm-Tone** *(also used for Response)*

JOSEPH GELINEAU (adapt.)

*v. 2 only*

**Pss 41/2**

**Response**  Líke the déer that yéarns
for rúnning stréams,
só my sóul is yéarning
for yóu, my Gód.

1. My sóul is thírsting for Gód,
the Gód of my lífe;
whén can I énter and sée
the fáce of Gód?  ℞.

2. Thése things will Í remémber
as I póur out my sóul:
how I would léad the rejóicing crówd
into the hóuse of Gód,
amid críes of gládness and thanksgíving,
the thróng wild with jóy.  ℞.

3. O sénd forth your líght and your trúth;
let thése be my gúide.
Let them bríng me to your hóly móuntain
to the pláce where you dwéll.  ℞.

4. And I will cóme to the áltar of Gód,
the Gód of my jóy.
My redéemer, I will thánk you on the hárp,
O Gód, my Gód.  ℞.

# EASTER VIGIL, 7TH PSALM, alternative
*See 5th Sunday of Lent, Year B, p.114*

# EASTER VIGIL MASS and EASTER SUNDAY

**Response, Easter Day**      1st SETTING      GEOFFREY BOULTON SMITH

This day was made by the Lord; we re-joice and are glad.

**Response, Easter Vigil** *and beginning of v. 1 on* **Easter Day**

Psalm 117

Al - le - lu - ia, al - le - lu - ia, al - le - lu - ia! ___

1. Give
2. The
3. The

1. thanks to the Lord for he is good, for his love has no end. ___ Let the
2. Lord's 'right hand has triumphed; his right hand raised me up. ___ I shall not
3. stone which the builders re - jected has be-come ___ the corner - stone.

1. sons of Israel say: 'His love has no end.' R.
2. die, I shall live and re - count ___ his deeds. R.
3. This is the work of the Lord, a mar - vel in our eyes. R.

*The low D is to be played* instead *of the D above at the* Easter Vigil, *where the Alleluia becomes the people's Response.*

**Response, Easter Vigil**         **2nd SETTING**         CHRISTOPHER WALKER

Psalm 117

1. Give thanks to the Lord— for he is good for his love _____
2. The Lord's right hand— has tri-umphed;___ his right hand _____
3. The stone which the builders re-ject-ed___ has be-come the

1. ___has no end.___ Let the sons of Is-ra-el say: 'His love _____
2. raised me up.___ I shall not die, I shall live and re-count _____
3. cor-ner-stone. This is the work ___ of the Lord, a marvel ___

*mf*

*cresc. . . . . . . . . . . .* *f*

*Vigil* *Day*

1. ___has no end, his love _____ has no end.'___ Al-le-
2. ___his deeds, re-count _____ his deeds.___ Al-le-
3. ___ in our eyes, a marvel _____ in our eyes. ___ Al-le-

*f* *f*

## 2ND SUNDAY OF EASTER, Years A, B and C
### 1st SETTING

**Response**

PAUL INWOOD

**Tone for other verses** *(may also be used for v. 1 with the pointing given below)*

**Ps 117**

1.  Let the sons of Israel | say:
    'His love has no | end.'
    Let the sons of Aaron | say:
    'His love has no | end.'
    Let those who fear the | Lord say:
    'His love has no | end.'  ℟.

**1a.  *Year A only***
I was thrust, thrust down and | falling
but the Lord was my | helper.
The Lord is my strength and my | song;
he was my | saviour.
There are shouts of joy and | victory
in the tents of the | just.  ℟.

**1b.  *Year B only***
The Lord's right hand has | triumphed;
his right hand raised me | up.
I shall not die, I shall | live
and recount his | deeds.
I was punished, I was punished by the | Lord,
but not doomed to | die.  ℟.

2.  The stone which the builders re|jected
    has become the | corner-stone.
    This is the work of the | Lord,
    a marvel in our | eyes.
    This day was made by the | Lord;
    we rejoice and are | glad.  ℟.

3.  *Year C only*
    O Lord, grant us sal|vation;
    O Lord, grant suc|cess.
    Blessed in the name of the | Lord
    is he who | comes.
    We bless you from the house of the | Lord;
    the Lord God is our | light.  ℟.

**Response**                    2nd SETTING                    GEOFFREY BOULTON SMITH

Give   thanks  to the Lord for He is   good,   for his  love has has no   end.

**Psalm-Tone**

# 3RD SUNDAY OF EASTER, YEAR A
## 13th Sunday of the Year, Year C
### 1st SETTING

ROBERT SHERLAW JOHNSON

**Response, 3 Easter A**                    **Alternative Response**

Show us, Lord, the path of life.    'Al - le - lu - ia!

**Response, 13 Year C**

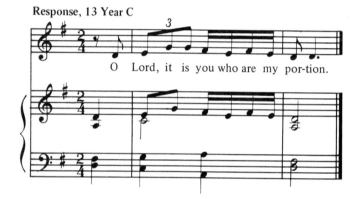

O Lord, it is you who are my por-tion.

**Psalm-Tone**

*Omit in v. 4*

**Ps 15**

1. Presérve | me, Gód, I take ré|fuge in | yóu.
   I sáy to the Lórd: 'You | are my | Gód.
   O Lórd, it is yóu who are my | pórtion • and | cúp;
   it is yóu yoursélf | who áre my | príze.' ℟.

2. I will | bléss the Lórd who | gíves me | cóunsel,
   who even at níght di|récts my | héart.
   Í keep the Lórd | éver in • my | síght:
   since hé is at my ríght hand, | Í shall stand | fírm. ℟.

3. And so | my héart rejóices, my | sóul is | glád;
   even my bódy shall | rést in | sáfety.
   For yóu will not léave my sóul a|mong the | déad,
   nor lét your belóved knów de|cáy. ℟.

4. Yóu will | shów me the | páth of | lífe,
   the fúllness of | jóy in • your | présence,
   at yóur right hánd háp|piness for | éver. ℟.

Response, 3 Easter A

BILL TAMBLYN

Moderate

Show us, Lord, the path of life.

Alternative Response

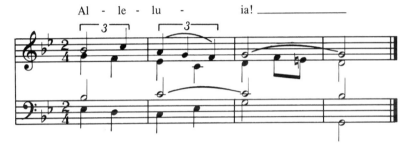

Al - le - lu - ia! _____

Response, 13 Year C

Calm

O Lord, it is you who are my por - tion.

Psalm-Tone

*Omit in v. 4*

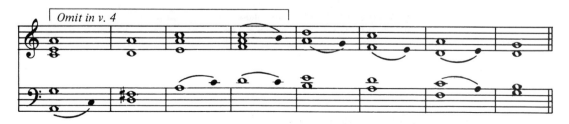

# 4TH SUNDAY OF EASTER, YEAR A
*See 4th Sunday of Lent, p.40.*

# 5TH SUNDAY OF EASTER, YEAR A
## 19th Sunday of the Year, Year C
### 1st SETTING

**Response, 5 Easter A**                                            BILL TAMBLYN

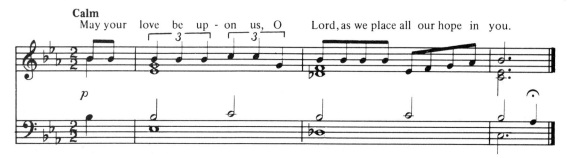

**Alternative Response**

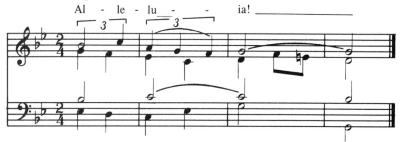

**Psalm-Tone**                                              JOSEPH GELINEAU

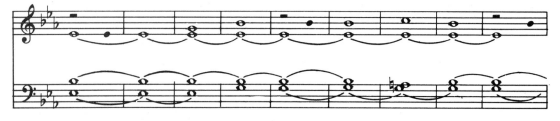

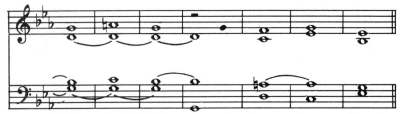

**Ps 32**

1. *5 Easter A only*
Ring out your jóy to the Lórd, O you júst;
for praise is fítting for lóyal héarts.
Give thánks to the Lórd upon the hárp,
with a tén-stringed lúte sing him sóngs. ℞.

1. *19 Year C only*
Ring out your jóy to the Lórd, O you júst;
for praise is fítting for lóyal héarts.
They are háppy whose Gód is the Lórd,
the péople he has chósen as his ówn. ℞.

2. *5 Easter A only*
*The wórd of the Lórd is fáithful
and áll his wórks to be trústed.
The Lórd loves jústice and ríght
and fílls the éarth with his lóve. ℞.

*The* Lectionary *erroneously begins this verse with the word 'For'.*

3. The Lórd looks on thóse who revére him,
    on thóse who hópe in his lóve,
    to réscue their sóuls from déath,
    to kéep them alíve in fámine.   ℟.

4. *19 Year C only*
    Our sóul is wáiting for the Lórd.
    The Lórd is our hélp and our shíeld.
    May your lóve be upón us O Lórd,
    as we pláce all our hópe in yóu.   ℟.

Response       2nd SETTING       CHRISTOPHER WALKER

♩. = c. 60

May your love be up-on us, O Lord,— as we place all our hope in you.

Psalm 32

Boldly, *f*

1. Ring out your joy to the Lord, O you just; for praise is fitting for loy-al hearts.
2. For the word of the Lord— is faithful and all his works to be trusted.
3. The Lord looks on those who re-vere him, on those who hope in his love,

1. Give thanks to the Lord up-on the harp, with a ten-stringed lute sing him songs. ℟.
2. The Lord loves jus-tice and right and fills the earth with his love. ℟.
3. to rescue their souls from death, to keep them a-live— in famine. ℟.

# 6TH SUNDAY OF EASTER, YEAR A
## 14th Sunday of the Year, Year C

**Response**　　　　　　　　　1st SETTING　　　　　　　JAMES WALSH

Allegro Cry out with joy, al - le - lu - ia! Cry out with joy to

(Org.)

God all the earth.

**Alternative Response**

Al - le - lu - ia, al - le - lu - ia!

**Psalm 65**

1. Cry out with joy to God all the earth,　O sing to the
2. 'Before you all the earth_ shall bow;　shall sing to you
3. He turned the sea in - to dry land,　they passed through the
4. Come and hear, all_who fear God.　I will tell what he

1. glo - ry of his name.　O render him glo - rious praise.
2. sing___ to your name!'　Come and see the works_ of God,
3. ri - ver dry - shod.　Let our joy then be_ in him;
4. did___ for my soul:　Blessed be God who did not re-ject_ my prayer

1. Say to God: 'How tre - men - dous your deeds!' ℞.
2. tremendous his deeds a - mong men. ℞.
3. he rules for e - ver by his might. ℞.
4. nor with - hold his love from me. ℞.

2nd SETTING

**Response** BILL TAMBLYN

Quite fast

*or:* Al - le - lu - ia, al - le - lu - ia!
Cry out with joy to God all the earth.

**Psalm-Tone** JOSEPH GELINEAU

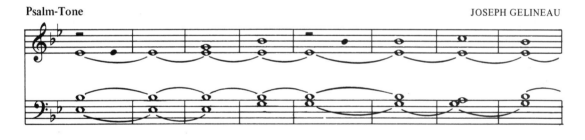

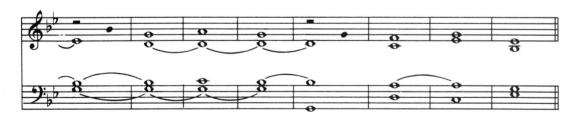

**Ps 65**

1. Cry out with jóy to Gód all the éarth,
   O síng to the glóry of his náme.
   O rénder him glórious práise.
   Say to Gód: 'How treméndous your déeds!' ℞.

2. 'Before yóu all the éarth shall bów;
   shall síng to you, síng to your náme!'
   Cóme and see the wórks of Gód,
   tremendous his deeds among men. ℞.

3. He túrned the séa into drý land,
   they pássed through the ríver dry-shód.
   Let our jóy thén be in hím;
   he rúles for éver by his míght, ℞.

4. Come and héar, áll who fear Gód.
   I will téll what he díd for my sóul:
   Blessed be Gód who did nót reject my práyer
   nor withhóld his lóve from mé. ℞.

# 7TH SUNDAY OF EASTER, YEAR A
## 3rd Sunday of the Year, Year A

**Response, 7 Easter A**      GEOFFREY BOULTON SMITH

*When guitars are used with organ, guitarists omit this chord.

I am sure I shall see the Lord's goodness in the land of the liv-ing.

land of the liv-ing. land of the liv-ing.

**Alternative Response, 7 Easter A**

Al-le-lu-ia,— al-le-lu-ia! -lu-ia!

**Response, 3 Year A**

The Lord——— is my light and my help. light and my help.

Psalm-Tone

JOSEPH GELINEAU, adapted G.B.S.

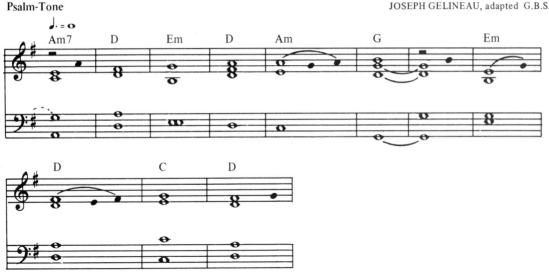

**Ps 26**

1. The Lórd is my líght and my hélp;
   whóm shall I féar?
   The Lórd is • the strónghold • of my lífe;
   before whóm shall • I shrínk? ℟.

2. There is óne thing I ásk of the Lórd,
   for thís I lóng,
   to líve in • the hóuse of the Lórd,
   all the dáys of • my lífe,
   to sávour • the swéetness • of the Lórd,
   to behóld his témple. ℟.

3. *7 Easter A only*
   O Lórd, hear my vóice when I cáll;
   have mércy and ánswer.
   Of yóu my héart has spóken:
   'Séek his fáce.' ℟.

3. *3 Year A only*
   I am súre I shall sée the Lord's góodness
   in the lánd of the líving.
   Hope in hím, hold fírm and take héart.
   Hópe in • the Lórd! ℟.

*An alternative setting will be found on p. 157.*

# ASCENSION, YEARS A, B and C

**Response**

SHAUN MacCARTHY

God goes up with shouts of joy; the Lord goes up with trumpet blast.

*Last time*

*to verses*

blast.

**Psalm 46**

1. All peo-ples, clap your hands, cry to God with shouts of

2. God goes up with shouts of joy; the Lord goes up with trum-pet

3. God is king of all the earth. Sing praise with all your

Org.

## PENTECOST
### (Easter Vigil 1st Psalm)
### 1st SETTING

ALAN REES

**Psalm-Tone**            LAURENCE BÉVENOT

*Pentecost (only)*

Ps 103

1. Bless the | Lord, my | soul!
   Lord God, how | great you | are.
   How many are your | works, O | Lord!
   The earth is full | of your | riches. ℟.

2. You take back your spi|rit, they | die,
   returning to the dust from | which they | came.
   You send forth your spirit, they | are cre|ated;
   and you renew the face | of the | earth. ℟.

3. May the glory of the Lord | last for | ever!
   May the Lord rejoice | in his | works!
   May my thoughts be pleas|ing to | him.
   I find my joy | in the | Lord. ℟.

## 2nd SETTING

**Response**            JOHN AINSLIE

Send forth your spi - rit, O Lord, and re - new the face_ of the earth.

**Psalm-Tone**

*Easter Vigil 1 (only)*

Ps 103

1. Bless the | Lord, my | soul!
   Lord God, how | great you | are,
   clothed in majes|ty and | glory,
   wrapped in light as | in a | robe! ℟.

2. You founded the earth | on its | base,
   to stand firm from | age to | age.
   You wrapped it with the ocean | like a | cloak:
   the waters stood higher | than the | mountains. ℟.

3. You make springs gush forth | from the | valleys:
   they flow in be|tween the | hills.
   On their banks dwell the | birds of | heaven;
   from the branches they | sing their | song. ℟.

4. From your dwelling you wa|ter the | hills;
   earth drinks its fill | of your | 'gift.
   You make the grass grow | for the | cattle
   and the plants to | serve man's | needs. ℟.

5. How many are your | works, O | Lord!
   In wisdom you have | made them | all.
   The earth is full | of your | riches.
   Bless the | Lord, my | soul! ℟.

*Either setting may be used with each set of verses.*

# TRINITY SUNDAY, YEAR A
## 1st SETTING

**Response**　　　　　　　　　　　　　　　　　　　　　　JAMES WALSH

**Psalm-Tone**　　　　　　　　　　　　　　　　　　　　　　STANBROOK

**Dan 3**

1. You are blest, Lord God of our | fathers.
   To you glory and praise for | ever|more.
   Blest your | glorious | name.
   To you glory and praise for | ever|more.　℟.

2. You are blest in the temple of your | glory.
   To you glory and praise for | ever|more.
   You are blest on the throne | of your | kingdom.
   To you glory and praise for | ever|more.　℟.

3. You are blest who gaze into the | depths.
   To you glory and praise for | ever|more.
   You are blest in the firma|ment of | heaven.
   To you glory and praise for | ever|more.　℟.

Response

*Trinity Sunday A*

2nd SETTING

PAUL INWOOD

R. To you glo-ry and praise for e - ver - more. To

more. 1. You are blest, Lord God of our fa - thers.__ R. *To*

blest in the temple of your glo - ry.__ R. *To*

blest who gaze in - to the depths.__ R. *To*

Psalm: Dan 3

*you glo-ry and praise for e - ver - more.__ Blest your glo - rious*

*you glo-ry and praise for e - ver - more.__ You are blest on the throne of your*

*you glo-ry and praise for e - ver - more.__ You are blest in the fir-ma-ment of*

1. name.— R. To you glo-ry and praise for e - ver - more.— 2. You are

2. king-dom.— R. To you glo-ry and praise for e - ver more.— 3. You are

3. heaven.— R. To you glo-ry and praise for e - ver - more.

*Last time:*

*poco rall.*

## CORPUS CHRISTI, YEAR A
*See 2nd Sunday after Christmas, p.28.*

## 2ND SUNDAY OF THE YEAR, YEAR A
### 2nd Sunday of the Year, Year B

**Response**                                                                PAUL INWOOD

Here I am, Lord! I come to do your will.

**Psalm-Tone**

**Ps 39**

1. I waited, I waited | for the | Lord
   and he stooped down to me; he | heard my | cry.
   He put a new song in|to my | mouth,
   praise | of our | God.   ℞.

2. You do not ask for sacri|fice and | offerings,
   but an | open | ear.
   You do not ask for holo|caust and | victim.
   Instead, | here am | I.   ℞.

3. In the scroll of the book | it stands | written
   that I should | do your | will.
   My God, I delight | in your | law
   in the depth | of my | heart.   ℞.

4. Your justice I | have pro|claimed
   in the | great as|sembly.
   My lips I | have not | sealed;
   you know | it, O | Lord.   ℞.

# 3RD SUNDAY OF THE YEAR, YEAR A
*See 7th Sunday of Easter, Year A, p.62;*
*also 2nd Sunday of Lent, Year C, p.157.*

# 4TH SUNDAY OF THE YEAR, YEAR A

**Response**                                                          GEOFFREY BOULTON SMITH

**Alternative Response**

**Psalm-Tone**

**Ps 145**

1. It is he who keeps | faith for | ever,
   who is just to those who | are op|pressed.
   It is he who gives bread | to the | hungry,
   the Lord, who sets pri|soners | free. ℞.

2. It is the Lord who gives sight | to the | blind,
   who raises up those who | are bowed | down,
   the Lord, who pro|tects the | stranger
   and upholds the wi|dow and | orphan. ℞.

3. It is the Lord who | loves the | just
   but thwarts the path | of the | wicked.
   The Lord will | reign for | ever,
   Zion's God, from | age to | age. ℞.

*Another setting will be found on p.15.*

## 5TH SUNDAY OF THE YEAR, YEAR A

**Response**

MARTIN HALL

The good man is a light in the dark-ness for the up - right.

**Psalm-Tone**

**Ps 111**

1. He is a light in the darkness | for the | upright:
   he is generous, merci|ful and | just.
   The good man takes pi|ty and | lends,
   he conducts his affairs | with | honour. ℞.

2. The just man will | never | waver:
   he will be remem|bered for | ever.
   He has no fear of | evil | news;
   with a firm heart he trusts in | the | Lord. ℞.

3. With a steadfast heart he | will not | fear;
   open-handed, he gives | to the | poor;
   his justice stands | firm for | ever.
   His head will be raised | in | glory. ℞.

# 6TH SUNDAY OF THE YEAR, YEAR A

**Response**                           MARTIN HALL

                                       JOSEPH GELINEAU
**Psalm-Tone**                                   (slightly adapted)

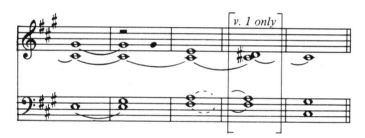

**Ps 118**

1. They are háppy whose lífe is blámeless,
   who fóllow God's láw!
   They are háppy those who dó his wíll,
   seeking hím with áll their héarts. ℟.

2. Yóu have laid dówn your précepts
   to be obéyed with cáre.
   Máy my fóotsteps be fírm
   to obéy your státutes. ℟.

3. Bless your sérvant and Í shall líve
   and obéy your wórd.
   Open my eyés that Í may consíder
   the wónders of your láw. ℟.

4. Téach me the demánds of your státutes
   and I will kéep them to the énd.
   Tráin me to obsérve your láw,
   to kéep it with my héart. ℟.

# 7TH SUNDAY OF THE YEAR, YEAR A
## 8th Sunday of the Year, Year B
## 7th Sunday of the Year, Year C
### (Easter Vigil 1st Psalm, alternative)
### 1st SETTING

**Response**

GEOFFREY BOULTON SMITH

The Lord_____ is com - pas - sion and love.
(Easter Vigil)The Lord_____ fills the earth with his love.
- pas - sion and love. earth with his love.

**Psalm-Tone**

JOSEPH GELINEAU (arr. G.B.S.)

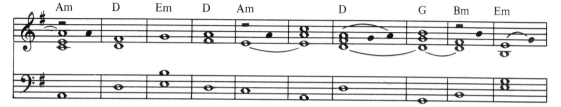

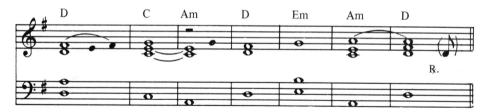

*Easter Vigil 1B*

**Ps 102**

1. My sóul, give thánks to the Lórd,
   all my béing, bléss his • holy náme.
   My sóul, give thánks to the Lórd
   and néver forgét all his bléssings.  ℞.

2. It is hé who forgíves all your gúilt,
   who héals every óne of your ílls,
   who redéems your lífe from the gráve,
   who crówns you with lóve and compássion.  ℞.

3. The Lórd is compássion and lóve,
   slow to ánger and rích in mércy.
   He does not tréat us • accórding • to our síns
   nor repáy us accórding to our fáults.  ℞.

4. As fár as the éast is from the wést
   so fár does he remóve our síns.
   As a fáther has • compássion • on his sóns,
   the Lord has píty on thóse who féar him.  ℞.

**Ps 32**

1. The wórd of the Lórd is fáithful
   and áll his wórks to be trústed.
   The Lórd loves jústice and ríght
   and fílls the éarth with his lóve.  ℞.

2. By his wórd the héavens were máde,
   by the bréath of his móuth all the stárs.
   He colléts the wáves of the ócean;
   he stóres up the dépths of the séa.  ℞.

3. They are háppy, whose Gód is the Lórd,
   the péople he has chósen • as his ówn.
   From the héavens the Lórd looks fórth,
   he sées all the chíldren of mén.  ℞.

4. Our sóul is wáiting for the Lórd.
   The Lórd is our hélp and our shíeld.
   May your lóve be • upón us, O Lórd,
   as we pláce all our hópe in yóu.  ℞.

*7th Sunday of Year A*

2nd SETTING

**Response**

CHRISTOPHER McCURRY

The Lord is com - pas - sion and love. _____
(Vigil:) The Lord fills the earth with his love. _____

**Psalm 102**

1. My soul, give thanks to the Lord, all my being, bless his ho - ly name. My
2. It is he who forgives all your guilt, who heals every one of your ills, who re -
3. The Lord is compas - sion and love, slow to anger and rich in mercy. He does not
4. As far as the east is from the west, so far does he re-move our sins. As a

1. soul, give thanks to the Lord and never forget all his blessings. R.
2. -deems your life from the grave, who crowns you with love and com-passion. R.
3. treat us according to our sins, nor re - pay us according to our faults. R.
4. father has compassion on his sons, the Lord has pity on those who fear him. R.

**Psalm 32** *Easter Vigil*

1. The word of the Lord is faithful and all his works to be trusted. The
2. By his word the heavens were made, by the breath of his mouth all the stars. He col-
3. They are happy, whose God is the Lord, the people he has chosen as his own. From the
4. Our soul is waiting for the Lord. The Lord is our help and our shield. May your

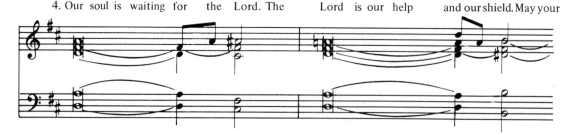

1. Lord loves jus - tice and right and fills the earth with his love R.
2. -lects the waves of the oceans; he stores up the depths of the sea. R.
3. heavens the Lord looks forth, he sees all the child - ren of men. R.
4. love be upon us, O Lord, as we place all our hope in you. R.

**3rd SETTING**
*(not Easter Vigil)*

**Response**        LAURENCE BÉVENOT

The Lord is com-pass-ion and love.

**Psalm 102**

1. My soul, give thanks to the Lord, all my being, bless his ho - ly name.
3. The Lord is com-pas - sion and love, slow to anger and rich in mercy.

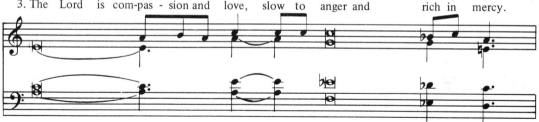

1. My soul, give thanks to the Lord, and never for - get all his blessings. R.
3. He does not treat us according to our sins, nor re-pay us ac -cording to our faults. R.

2. It is he who for - gives all your guilt, who heals every one of your ills,
4. As far as the east is from the west, so far does he re-move our sins,

2. who re-deems your life from the grave,    who crowns you with love and com - pas-sion. ℟.
4. as a father has compassion on his sons,    the Lord has pity on those who fear him. ℟.

## 8TH SUNDAY OF THE YEAR, YEAR A

**Response**                               MARTIN HALL

In God a - lone is my soul at rest.

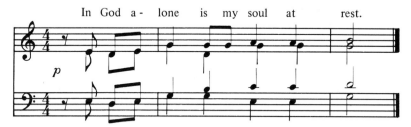

**Psalm-Tone**

**Ps 61**

1. In God alone is my | soul at | rest;
   my help | comes from | him.
   He alone is my rock, | my | stronghold,
   my fortress: I | stand | firm.   ℟.

2. In God alone be at | rest, my | soul;
   for my hope | comes from | him.
   He alone is my rock, | my | stronghold,
   my fortress: I | stand | firm.   ℟.

3. In God is my safe|ty and | glory,
   the rock | of my | strength.
   Take refuge in God all | you | people.
   Trust him at all times. Pour out your hearts | be|fore him.   ℟.

## 9TH SUNDAY OF THE YEAR, YEAR A

**Response**                               MARTIN HALL

Be a rock of ref - uge for me, O Lord.

*(Bracketed naturals last time only)*

**Psalm-Tone**

A. GREGORY MURRAY

**Ps 30**

1. In you, O Lord, | I take | refuge.
   Let me never be | put to | shame.
   In your justice, | set me | free,
   hear me and speed|ily | rescue me.  ℟.

2. Be a rock of re|fuge for | me,
   a mighty strong|hold to | save me,
   for you are my | rock, my | stronghold.
   For your name's sake, lead | me and | guide me.  ℟.

3. Let your face shine | on your | servant.
   Save me | in your | love.
   Be strong, let your | heart take | courage,
   all who hope | in the | Lord.  ℟.

# 10TH SUNDAY OF THE YEAR, YEAR A

## 1st SETTING

**Response**

MARTIN HALL

I will show God's sal - vat - ion to the up - right.

**Psalm-Tone**

**Ps 49**

1. The God of gods, the Lord, has spoken and sum|moned the | earth,
   from the rising of the sun | to its | setting.
   'I find no fault | with your | sacrifices,
   your offerings are al|ways be|fore me.  ℟.

2. 'Were I hungry, I | would not | tell you,
   for I own the world and | all it | holds.
   Do you think I eat the | flesh of | bulls,
   or drink the | blood of | goats?  ℟.

3. 'Pay your sacrifices of thanksgiv|ing to | God
   and render him your | votive | offerings.
   Call on me in the day | of dis|tress.
   I will free you and | you shall | honour me.'  ℟.

2nd SETTING

**Response**                                    JAMES WALSH

I will show God's sal - vat - ion to the up - right.

**Psalm-Tone**                              LAURENCE BÉVENOT

Ps 49

1.  The God of gods, the Lord, has spoken and sum|moned the | earth,
    from the rising of the sun | to its | setting.
    'I find no fault | with your | sacrifices,
    your offerings are al|ways be|fore me.   ℟.

2.  'Were I hungry, I | would not | tell you,
    for I own the world and | all it | holds.
    Do you think I eat the | flesh of | bulls,
    or drink the | blood of | goats?   ℟.

3.  'Pay your sacrifices of thanksgiv|ing to | God
    and render him your | votive | offerings.
    Call on me in the day | of dis|tress.
    I will free you and | you shall | honour me.'   ℟.

# 11TH SUNDAY OF THE YEAR, YEAR A
## 4th Sunday of Easter, Year C

**Response**                                    MICHAEL COY

We are his peo - ple, the sheep___ of his flock.___

Guitars capo fret 3   G   D   Bm   Em   Em7   Am   D

**Alternative Response, 4 Easter C**    A. GREGORY MURRAY

Al - le - lu - ia, al - le - lu - ia, al - le - lu - ia!

**Psalm-Tone**    JOSEPH GELINEAU

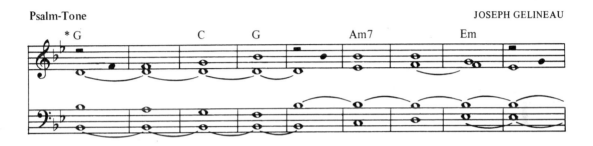

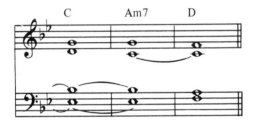

*Guitar chords capo 3. The chords cannot be used with the organ accompaniment.*

**Ps 99**

1.  *Cry out with jóy to the Lórd, all the éarth.
    Sérve the Lórd with gládness.
    Come befóre him, sínging for jóy. ℟.

2.  Know that hé the Lórd is Gód.
    He máde us, we belóng to hím,
    we are his péople, the shéep of his flóck. ℟.

3.  Indéed, how góod is the Lórd,
    etérnal his mérciful lóve.
    He is fáithful from áge to áge. ℟.

*The Lectionary for the 11th Sunday of Year A omits the first line of verse 1. If this is adhered
to, the first part of the tone must also be omitted.*

# 12TH SUNDAY OF THE YEAR, YEAR A

**Response**                                            MARTIN HALL

In your great love, ans-wer me, O God.

**Psalm-Tone**

Ps 68

1.  It is for you that I | suffer | taunts,
    that shame co|vers my | face,
    that I have become a stranger | to my | brothers,
    an alien to my own | mother's | sons.
    I burn with zeal for | your | house
    and taunts against you | fall on | me.  ℟.

2.  This is my | prayer to | you,
    my prayer | for your | favour.
    In your great love, answer | me, O | God,
    with your help that | never | fails:
    Lord, answer, for your love | is | kind;
    in your compassion, | turn to|wards me.  ℟.

3.  The poor when they see it | will be | glad
    and God-seeking hearts | will re|vive;
    for the Lord listens | to the | needy
    and does not spurn his servants | in their| chains.
    Let the heavens and the earth give | him | praise,
    the sea and all its | living | creatures.  ℟.

# . 13TH SUNDAY OF THE YEAR, YEAR A
## 4th Sunday of Advent, Year B

                            1st SETTING

**Response**                                  DENIS McCARTHY

I will sing for e - ver of your love, O Lord.

**Psalm-Tone**                                                LAURENCE BÉVENOT

Ps 88

1.  I will sing for ever of your | love, O | Lord;
    through all ages my mouth will pro|claim your | truth.
    Of this I am sure, that your love | lasts for | ever,
    that your truth is firmly established | as the | heavens.   ℞.

*13th Sunday of Year A*

2.  Happy the people who acclaim | such a | king,
    who walk, O Lord, in the light | of your | face,
    who find their joy every day | in your | name,
    who make your justice the source | of their | bliss.   ℞.

3.  For it is you, O Lord, who are the glory | of their | strength;
    it is by your favour that our might | is ex|alted:
    for our ruler is in the keeping | of the | Lord;
    our king is in the keeping of the Holy | One of | Israel.   ℞.

*4 Advent B*

2.  'I have made a covenant | with my | chosen one;
    I have sworn to Da|vid my | servant:
    I will establish your dynas|ty for | ever
    and set up your throne | through all | ages.'   ℞.

3.  He will say to me: 'You | are my | father,
    my God, the | rock who | saves me.'
    I will keep my love | for him | always;
    for him my covenant | shall en|dure.   ℞.

## 2nd SETTING

**Response**                                                  MARTIN HALL

**Psalm-Tone**

# 14TH SUNDAY OF THE YEAR, YEAR A
## 31st Sunday of the Year, Year C

**Response**                                    MARTIN HALL

I will bless your name for e - ver, O God my King.

**Psalm-Tone**

**Ps 144**

1. I will give you glo|ry, O God my | King,
   I will bless your | name for | ever.
   I will bless you day | after | day
   and praise your | name for | ever. ℞.

2. The Lord is kind | and full of com|passion,
   slow to anger, abound|ing in | love.
   How good is the | Lord to | all,
   compassionate to | all his | creatures. ℞.

3. All your creatures | shall thank you, O | Lord,
   and your friends shall re|peat their | blessing.
   They shall speak of the glory | of your | reign
   and declare your | might, O | God. ℞.

4. The Lord is faith|ful in all his | words
   and loving in | all his | deeds.
   The Lord supports | all who | fall
   and raises all who | are bowed | down. ℞.

# 15TH SUNDAY OF THE YEAR, YEAR A

## 1st SETTING

**Response**                                    PAUL JOHNSTONE

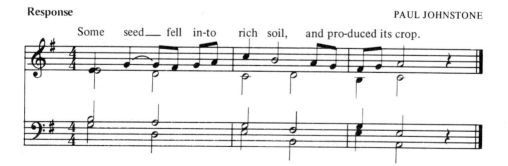

Some seed___ fell in-to rich soil, and pro-duced its crop.

Psalm 64

1. You care for the earth, give it wa-ter, you fill it with rich-es. Your
2. And thus you provide for the earth;— you drench its fur-rows, you

1. ri - ver in heaven brims o - ver to pro-vide its grain._____ R̥.
2. le-vel it,— soft-en it with showers, you_ bless its growth._____ R̥.

3. You crown the year with your good-ness. A - bun-dance flows in your steps, in the

past-ures of the wild - er - ness it flows._____ R̥.

4. The hills are gird - ed with joy, the mea-dows cov-ered with flocks, the

val - leys are decked_ with wheat. They shout for joy,    yes,_____ they    sing.   R.

**Response**            2nd SETTING           CHRISTOPHER WALKER

*Last time only*

Some seed    fell in - to    rich soil    and pro-duced its crop.

**Psalm 64**

*Gently*

1. You care for the earth, give    it    water,      you        fill it      with riches.
2. And thus you pro - vide for the   earth;     you        drench     its furrows,

3. You crown the year with your goodness.   [                    ]
4. The   hills   are girded   with joy,     the meadows covered     with flocks,

*(8′ only)*

1. Your river in heaven brims over     to pro     -     vide   its   grain.   R.
2. you level it, soften it with showers,    you         bless   its   growth   R.

3. Abundance      flows in your steps,      in the pastures of the wilderness it flows.   R.
4. the valleys are decked    with wheat.     They shout for joy, yes,    they sing.   R.

# 16TH SUNDAY OF THE YEAR, YEAR A

### 1st SETTING

**Response**                                          PAUL INWOOD

**Psalm-Tone**

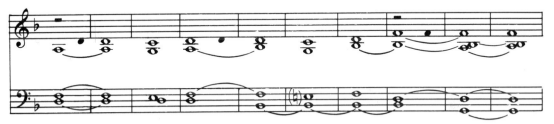

**Ps 85**

1. O Lórd, you are góod | and for|gíving,
   full of lóve to | áll who | cáll.
   Give héed, O Lórd, | to my | práyer
   and atténd to thé sóund | of my | vóice.  R.

2. All the nátions shall cóme | to a|dóre you
   and glórify your | náme, O | Lórd:
   for you are gréat and do | márvel•lous | déeds,
   yóu who a|lóne are | Gód.  R.

3. But yóu, God of mércy | and com|pássion,
   slów to án|ger, O | Lórd,
   abóunding in | lóve and | trúth,
   túrn and take pí|ty on | mé.  R.

### 2nd SETTING

**Response**                                          MARTIN HALL

**Psalm-Tone**                              A. GREGORY MURRAY

# 17TH SUNDAY OF THE YEAR, YEAR A

1st SETTING
MARTIN HALL

**Response**

Lord, how I love your law!

**Psalm-Tone**

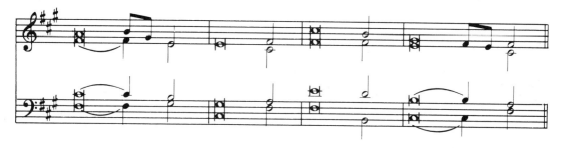

**Ps 118**

1. My part, I have re|solved, O | Lord,
   is to obey your | word.
   The law from your mouth means | more to me
   than sil|ver and | gold.  ℟.

2. Let your love be ready | to con|sole me
   by your promise to your | servant.
   Let your love come to me and I shall | live
   for your law is | my de|light.  ℟.

3. That is why I | love • your com|mands
   more than finest | gold.
   That is why I rule my life by your | precepts:
   I | hate false | ways.  ℟.

4. Your will is | wonderful • in|deed;
   therefore I o|bey it.
   The unfolding of your word gives | light
   and tea|ches the | simple.  ℟.

2nd SETTING
CHRISTOPHER WALKER

**Response**
Psalm 118

| Last time | To verses |
| --- | --- |
| | 1.  My |
| | 2.  Let your |
| | 3.  That is |
| | 4.  Your |

℟. Lord, how I love your law!

1. part, I have resolved, O Lord, is to o - bey your word.
2. love be ready to con - sole me by your promise to your servant.

3. why I love your com-mands more than fi - nest gold.
4. will is wonderful in - deed; therefore I o - bey it.

1. The law from your mouth means more to me
2. Let your love come to me and I shall live

3. That is why I rule my life by your precepts:
4. The un - folding of your word gives light

1. than sil - ver and gold. ℟.
2. for your law is my de - light. ℟.

3. I hate_____ false ways. ℟.
4. and tea - ches the simple. ℟.

# 18TH SUNDAY OF THE YEAR, YEAR A
## 17th Sunday of the Year, Year B

**Response**　　　　　　　　　　　　　　　　　　　　　　　TONY BARR

You o-pen wide your hand, O Lord, {you and} grant our de - sires.

**Psalm-Tone**

**Ps 144**

*18 Year A only*

1. The Lord is kind and full of | com|passion,
   slow to anger, a|bounding • in | love.
   How good is the | Lord to | all,
   compassionate to | all his | creatures.　R.

*17 Year B only*

1. All your creatures shall thank you, | O | Lord,
   and your friends shall re|peat their | blessing.
   They shall speak of the glory | of your | reign
   and declare your | might, O | God.　R.

2. The eyes of all creatures look | to | you
   and you give them their food | in due | time.
   You open | wide your | hand,
   grant the desires of | all who | live.　R.

3. The Lord is just in all | his | ways
   and loving in | all his | deeds.
   He is close to | all who | call him,
   who call on him | from their | hearts.　R.

*Note the slight difference in wording of the Response on the two days. Either wording may be chosen for use on both days.*

# 19TH SUNDAY OF THE YEAR, YEAR A
## 2nd Sunday of Advent, Year B
## 15th Sunday of the Year, Year B
### 1st SETTING

**Response**　　　　　　　　　　　　　　　　　　　　　　ELSIE WRIGHT

Let us see, O Lord, your mer - cy, and give us your sav - ing help.

**Psalm 84**

1. I will hear what the Lord God has to say, a voice that speaks of peace, *peace for his people.__ His help is near for those who fear him and his glory will dwell in our land. ℟.

\* *The Lectionary for 19th Sunday of Year A omits this line.*

2. Mercy and faithful - ness have met; justice and peace have em - braced. __ Faithfulness shall spring from the earth and jus - tice look down from heaven. ℟.

3. The Lord will make us prosper and our earth shall yield its fruit.__

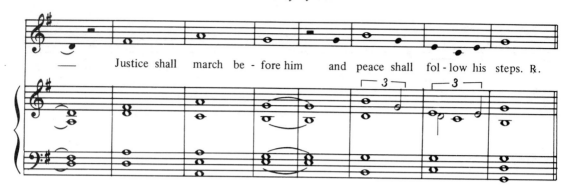

Justice shall march be - fore him and peace shall fol - low his steps. ℟.

## 2nd SETTING

**Response**

GEOFFREY BOULTON SMITH

**Gently flowing**

Let us see, O Lord, your mer-cy and give us your sav - ing help.

A    Em/G    F    A    D7    Am7    E

**Psalm 84**

**Lively** *(fairly free tempo)*

1. I will hear what the Lord God has to say, a voice that speaks of peace,

2. Mer-cy and faith-ful-ness have met; jus - tice and peace

3. The Lord will make us pros-per and our earth shall yield its fruit,

$E^7_4$    $B^7_4$ (or Bm7)    D6    E

1. peace for his peo - ple. His help is near for those who fear him and his

2. *(speaks of peace.)*
   *mp* have em - braced. Faith-ful-ness shall spring from the earth and

3. *p* yield its fruit. Jus - tice shall march be - fore him and

Am7   E⁷₄   Cmaj7   Am7

* For 19th Sunday of Year A, if desired.

1. glo - ry will dwell in our land. ℟.

2. jus - tice look down ＿ from heaven. ℟.

3. peace shall fol - low his steps. ℟.

F   Dm   E

# 20TH SUNDAY OF THE YEAR, YEAR A
## 6th Sunday of Easter, Year C
### 1st SETTING

**Response**

HAROLD BARKER

(Al - le - lu - ia,    al -    le - lu - ia,    al - - le - lu - ia!)
Let the peo - ples praise you, O God; let    all    the peo - ples praise you.

**Psalm-Tone**

### Ps 66

1. O God, be gracious and | bless us
   ánd let your fáce shed its líght upon us.
   So will your ways be | known up•on | earth
   and all nations learn your | saving | help.  ℟.

2. Let the nations be glad and ex|ult
   fór you rule the wórld with jústice.
   With fairness you | rule the | peoples,
   you guide the | nations •on | earth.  ℟.

3. Let the peoples praise you, O | God;
   lét all the péoples práise you.
   May God still | give us • his | blessing
   till the ends of the | earth re|vere him.  ℟.

### 2nd SETTING

**Response**

CHRISTOPHER McCURRY

(Al - le - lu - ia,    al - le - lu - ia,____ al - le - lu - ia,    al - le lu - ia!)
Let the peo - ples praise you, O    God;____ let    all the    peo - ples praise you.

**Psalm 66**

1. O God, be gra - cious and bless us      and   let your face shed its
2. Let the nations be glad and ex - ult      for you   rule the
3. Let the peoples praise you, O God;      let   all   the

1. light up - on us.   So will your   ways be known   up - on   earth   and all
2. world with justice.   With   fairness you   rule   the   peoples,   you
3. peo - ples praise you.   May   God still give   us   his   blessing   till the

1. nations learn your   sav - ing help.   ℟.
2. guide   the   nat - tions on earth.   ℟.
3. ends   of   the   earth re - vere him.   ℟.

**Alternative tone for verses**

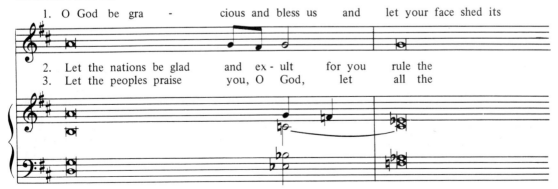

1. O God be gra -      cious and bless us      and   let your face shed its

2. Let the nations be glad      and ex - ult   for you   rule the
3. Let the peoples praise      you, O   God,   let   all   the

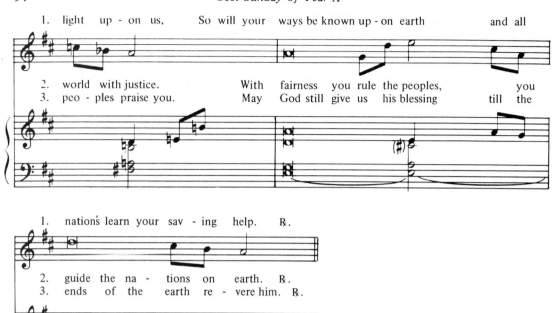

1. light up-on us, So will your ways be known up-on earth and all
2. world with justice. With fairness you rule the peoples, you
3. peo-ples praise you. May God still give us his blessing till the

1. nations learn your sav-ing help. ℟.
2. guide the na-tions on earth. ℟.
3. ends of the earth re-vere him. ℟.

## 21ST SUNDAY OF THE YEAR, YEAR A

**Response**          GEOFFREY BOULTON SMITH

**Gently flowing**

Your love, O Lord, is e-ter–nal, dis-card not the work of your hands.

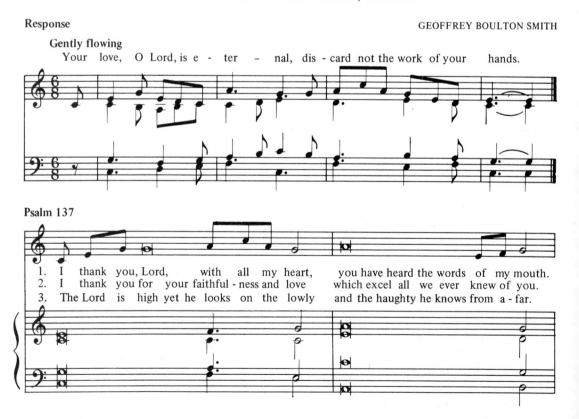

**Psalm 137**

1. I thank you, Lord, with all my heart, you have heard the words of my mouth.
2. I thank you for your faithful-ness and love which excel all we ever knew of you.
3. The Lord is high yet he looks on the lowly and the haughty he knows from a-far.

1. Be - fore the angels  I will bless you  I will adore before your ho - ly temple. ℞.
2. On the day I  called, you answered;  you increased the strength of my soul. ℞.
3. Your love, O Lord,  is e - ternal,  discard not the work of your hands. ℞.

## 22ND SUNDAY OF THE YEAR, YEAR A
### 32nd Sunday of the Year, Year A
### 12th Sunday of the Year, Year C

**Response**          1st SETTING          JAMES WALSH

For you — my soul is thirst - ing, O { God, / Lord } my God. _____

**Psalm-Tone**

Ps 62

1. O God, you are my God, for | you I | long;
   for you my | soul is | thirsting.
   My body | pines for | you
   like a dry, weary land | without | water.  ℞.

2. So I gaze on you | in the | sanctuary
   to see your strength | and your | glory.
   For your love is | better • than | life,
   my lips will | speak your | praise.  ℞.

3. So I will bless you | all my | life,
   in your name I will lift | up my | hands.
   My soul shall be | filled as with • a | banquet,
   my mouth shall | praise you • with | joy.  ℞.

*22 Year A and*
*12 Year C only*                    *32 Year A only*

4. For you have | been my | help;          4. On my bed | I re|member you.
   in the shadow of your wings | I re|joice.     O you I muse | through the | night
   My soul | clings to | you;               for you have | been my | help;
   your right hand | holds me | fast.  ℞.     in the shadow of your wings | I re|joice.  ℞.

*NB.*   *The Lectionary contains a variant in the wording of the Response for the 22nd*
       *Sunday of Year A; this is included in the music-settings for those who prefer to use it.*

2nd SETTING

**Response**                                                           MARTIN HALL

For you my soul is thirst - ing, O {God, / Lord} my God.

**Psalm-Tone**

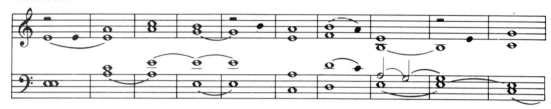

**Ps 62**

1.  O Gód, you are my Gód, for you I lóng;
    for yóu my sóul is thírsting.
    My bódy pínes for yóu
    like a drý, weary lánd without wáter.   ℞.

2.  So I gáze on yóu in the sánctuary
    to sée your stréngth and your glóry.
    For your lóve is bétter than lífe,
    my líps will spéak your práise.   ℞.

3.  So I will bléss you áll my lífe,
    in your náme I will líft up my hánds.
    My sóul shall be fílled as with a bánquet,
    my móuth shall práise you with jóy.   ℞.

*22 Year A and*
*12 Year C only*                            *32 Year A only*

4.  For yóu have béen my hélp;          4.  On my béd I remémber yóu.
    in the shádow of your wíngs I rejóice.     O yóu I múse through the níght
    My sóul clíngs to yóu;                      for yóu have béen my hélp;
    your ríght hand hólds me fást.   ℞.        in the shádow of your wíngs I rejóice.   ℞.

NB. *The Lectionary contains a variant in the wording of the Response for the 22nd*
    *Sunday of Year A; this is included in the music-settings for those who prefer to use it.*

3rd SETTING

**Response**                                                      ROGER BEVAN

For you my soul is ___ thirst-ing, O {God,}{Lord} my God.

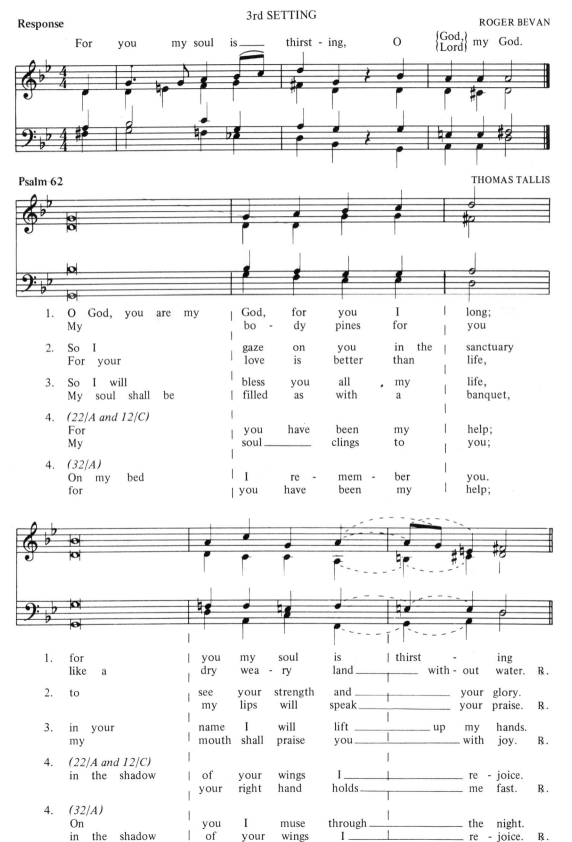

**Psalm 62**                                                  THOMAS TALLIS

1. O God, you are my | God, for you I | long;
   My | bo - dy pines for | you

2. So I | gaze on you in the | sanctuary
   For your | love is better than | life,

3. So I will | bless you all , my | life,
   My soul shall be | filled as with a | banquet,

4. *(22/A and 12/C)*
   For | you have been my | help;
   My | soul ___ clings to | you;

4. *(32/A)*
   On my bed | I re - mem - ber | you.
   for | you have been my | help;

1. for | you my soul is | thirst - ing
   like a | dry wea - ry land ___ with - out water. ℞.

2. to | see your strength and ___ your glory.
   my | lips will speak ___ your praise. ℞.

3. in your | name I will lift ___ up my hands.
   my | mouth shall praise you ___ with joy. ℞.

4. *(22/A and 12/C)*
   in the shadow | of your wings I ___ re - joice.
   your | right hand holds ___ me fast. ℞.

4. *(32/A)*
   On | you I muse through ___ the night.
   in the shadow | of your wings I ___ re - joice. ℞.

## 23RD SUNDAY OF THE YEAR, YEAR A
*See 3rd Sunday of Lent, Year A, p.36.*

## 24TH SUNDAY OF THE YEAR, YEAR A
### 3rd Sunday of Lent, Year C

### 1st SETTING

**Response, 24 Year A**                    GEOFFREY BOULTON SMITH

The Lord ___ is com-pas-ion and love, slow to an-ger and rich in mer-cy. ___

**Response, 3 Lent C**                    GEOFFREY BOULTON SMITH

The Lord is com - pas - sion and love. -pas - sion and love.

**Psalm-Tone**                    JOSEPH GELINEAU (arr. G.B.S.)

**Ps 102**

1. My sóul, give thánks | to the | Lórd,
   all my | béing, bléss his | holy | náme.
   My | sóul, give thánks | to the | Lórd
   and | néver forgét | all his | bléssings.   ℟.

2. It is hé who forgíves | all your | gúilt,
   who | héals every óne | of your | ílls,
   who re|déems your lífe | from the | gráve,
   who | crówns you with lóve | and com|pássion.   ℟.

*24 Year A only*

3. His wráth will cóme | to an | énd;
   he will | nót be ángry| for | éver.
   He does not | tréat us accórding | to our | síns
   nor re|páy us accórding | to our | fáults.  ℟.

4. For as the héavens are hígh a|bove the | éarth
   so | stróng is his lóve for | those who | féar him.
   As | fár as the éast is | from the | wést
   so | fár does he re|móve our | síns.  ℟.

*3 Lent C only*

3. The Lórd does | déeds of | jústice,
   gives | júdgement for áll who | are op|préssed.
   He | made knówn his | wáys to | Móses
   and his | déeds to | Ísrael's | sóns.  ℟.

4. The Lórd is compás|sion and | lóve,
   slow to | ánger and | rích in | mércy.
   For as the | héavens are hígh a|bove the | éarth
   so | stróng is his lóve for | those who | féar him.  ℟.

## 2nd SETTING

**Response, 24 Year A**  CHRISTOPHER McCURRY

**Response, 3 Lent C**

**Psalm-Tone**

*For an example of how the pointing fits with the McCurry psalm-tone, see 7th Sunday
of the Year, Year A, 2nd setting.*

# 25TH SUNDAY OF THE YEAR, YEAR A

**Response**                                         JAMES WALSH

**Alternative Response**                       MARTIN HALL

**Psalm-Tone**                                     JAMES WALSH

**Ps 144**

1. I will bless you day | after | day
   and praise your | name for | ever.
   The Lord is great, highly | to be | praised,
   his greatness | cannot • be | measured. ℞.

2. The Lord is kind and full | of com|passion,
   slow to anger, abound|ing in | love.
   How good is the | Lord to | all,
   compassionate to | all his | creatures. ℞.

3. The Lord is just in | all his | ways
   and loving in | all his | deeds.
   He is close to | all who | call him,
   who call on him | from their | hearts. ℞.

## 26TH SUNDAY OF THE YEAR, YEAR A

**Response**                                    JAMES WALSH

**Psalm-Tone**

Ps 24

1. Lord, make me | know your | ways.
   Lord, | teach me your | paths.
   Make me walk in your | truth, and | teach me:
   for you are God | my | saviour.  ℞.

2. Remember your | mercy, | Lord,
   and the love you have | shown from of | old.
   Do not remember the | sins of • my | youth.
   In your love remember | me,
   because of your goodness, | O | Lord.  ℞.

3. The Lord is | good and | upright.
   He shows the path | to those who | stray,
   he guides the humble | in the | right path;
   he teaches his way to | the | poor.  ℞.

## 27TH SUNDAY OF THE YEAR, YEAR A

**Response**

JAMES WALSH

The vine-yard of the Lord is the House of Is-rael.

**Psalm-Tone**

LAURENCE BÉVENOT

Ps 79

1. You brought a vine | out of | Egypt;
   to plant it you drove | out the | nations.
   It stretched out its branches | to the | sea,
   to the Great River it stretched | out
                      its | shoots.  ℞.

2. Then why have you broken | down
                      its | walls?
   It is plucked by all | who pass | by.
   It is ravaged by the boar | of the | forest,
   devoured by the beasts | of the | field.  ℞.

3. God of hosts, turn again, | we im|plore,
   look down from | heaven and | see.
   Visit this vine | and pro|tect it,
   the vine your right | hand has | planted.  ℞.

4. And we shall never forsake | you a|gain:
   give us life that we may call up|on your | name.
   God of hosts, | bring us | back;
   let your face shine on us and we | shall be | saved.  ℞.

## 28TH SUNDAY OF THE YEAR, YEAR A
*See 4th Sunday of Lent, Year A, p.40*

### 29TH SUNDAY OF THE YEAR, YEAR A

Response                                    GEOFFREY BOULTON SMITH

*[The soprano part may be omitted when the Response is sung in unison]*

Psalm-Tone                                  JOSEPH GELINEAU

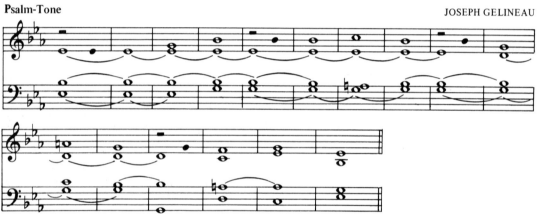

**Ps 95**

1. O síng a new sóng to the Lórd,
   síng to the Lórd all the éarth.
   Téll among the nátions his glóry
   and his wónders amóng all the péoples. ℟.

2. The Lord is gréat and wórthy of práise,
   to be féared abóve all góds;
   the góds of the héathens are náught.
   It was the Lórd who máde the héavens. ℟.

3. Give the Lórd, you fámilies of péoples,
   give the Lórd glóry and pówer,
   give the Lórd the glóry of his náme.
   Bring an óffering and énter his cóurts. ℟.

4. Wórship the Lórd in his témple.
   O éarth, trémble befóre him.
   Procláim to the nátions: 'God is kíng.'
   He will júdge the péoples in fáirness. ℟.

### 30TH SUNDAY OF THE YEAR, YEAR A
#### 31st Sunday of the Year, Year B

Response                                    JAMES WALSH

**Psalm-Tone**

**Ps 17**

1. I love you, Lord, | my | strength,
   my rock, my fort|ress, my̆ | saviour.
   My God is the rock | where I take | refuge;
   my shield, my mighty | help, my | stronghold.
   The Lord is worthy of all | praise:
   when I call I am saved from | my | foes.   ℟.

2. Long life to the | Lord, my | rock!
   Praised be | the God who | saves me.
   He has given great victories | to his | king
   and shown his love for his | a|nointed.   ℟.

## 31ST SUNDAY OF THE YEAR, YEAR A

### 1st SETTING

**Response**

JAMES WALSH

**Not too slow**

Guard my soul in peace be - fore you, O Lord.

**Psalm 130**

1. O Lord, my heart is not proud nor haugh-ty my eyes.

2. Tru - ly I have set my soul in si - lence and peace. A

3. O Is - rael, hope in the Lord both now and for e - ver. O

1. I have not gone af - ter things too great nor mar-vels be - yond    me.  ℟.

2, weaned , child on its mother's breast, even so is my soul. _____  ℟.

3. Is - rael, hope in the Lord both    now and for e - ver.___  ℟.

*Omit in v.3*

**Response**          2nd SETTING          PAUL INWOOD

Guard my soul in   peace be-fore you, O Lord.    *Last time*

**Psalm-Tone**

v.3
starts
here

(v.3)   (v.2)   (v.2)

**Ps 130**

1. O Lord, my heart is not | proud
   nor haughty my eyes.
   I have not gone after | things too | great
   nor marvels beyond me.  ℟.

2. Truly I have set my | soul
   in silence and peace.
   A weaned child on its | mother's | breast,
   even so is my soul.  ℟.

3. O Israel, | hope in the | Lord
   both now and for ever.  ℟.

## 32ND SUNDAY OF THE YEAR, YEAR A
*See 22nd Sunday of the Year, Year A, p.95.*

## 33RD SUNDAY OF THE YEAR, YEAR A
*See Holy Family, p.24.*

## LAST SUNDAY OF THE YEAR, YEAR A
### Solemnity of Christ the King

Response                                                          JAMES WALSH

The Lord is my shepherd; there is nothing I shall want.

Psalm-Tone

**Ps 22**

1.  The Lord | is my | shepherd;
    there is nothing | I shall | want.
    Fresh and | green are the | pastures
    where he | gives me re|pose.   ℞.

2.  Near restful wa|ters he | leads me,
    to revive my | drooping | spirit.
    He guides me a|long the right | path;
    he is | true to his | name.   ℞.

3.  You have prepared a ban|quet for | me
    in the sight | of my | foes.
    My head you have a|nointed with | oil;
    my cup | is over|flowing.
         *(Repeat entire psalm-tone)*
    Surely goodness and kind|ness shall | follow me
    all the days | of my | life.
    In the Lord's own | house shall I | dwell
    for | ever and | ever.   ℞.

*Verse layout above is as in the Lectionary. If desired, the Response may additionally
be sung halfway through v.3.*

# 1ST SUNDAY OF ADVENT, YEAR B
## 4th Sunday of Advent, Year C

### 1st SETTING

**Response**

PAUL INWOOD

1. Lord, rouse up your might, O Lord, come to our help. ℟.
2. Vis-it this vine and pro-tect it, ___ the vine your right hand has plant-ed. ℟.
3. nev-er for-sake you a - gain: give us life that we may call up-on your name. ℟.

*attacca ℟.*
*tempo primo*

**2nd SETTING**

JAMES WALSH

Response

God of hosts, bring us back; let your face shine on us and we shall be saved.

*\*Last time, optional C♯*

**Psalm-Tone**

**Ps 79**

1. O shepherd of | Israel, | hear us,
   shine forth from your | cherub•im | throne.
   O Lord, rouse | up your | might,
   O Lord, | come to our | help. ℟.

2. God of hosts, turn a|gain, we • im|plore,
   look down from | heaven and | see.
   Visit this vine | and pro|tect it,
   the vine your | right hand has | planted. ℟.

3. May your hand be on the | man you • have | chosen,
   the man you have | given • your | strength.
   And we shall never forsake | you a|gain:
   give us life that we may | call up•on your | name. ℟

## 2ND SUNDAY OF ADVENT, YEAR B
*See 19th Sunday of the Year, Year A, p. 88.*

## 3RD SUNDAY OF ADVENT, YEAR B

**Response**                 PAUL INWOOD

My soul re - joi - ces in my God.

**Psalm: Lk 1**

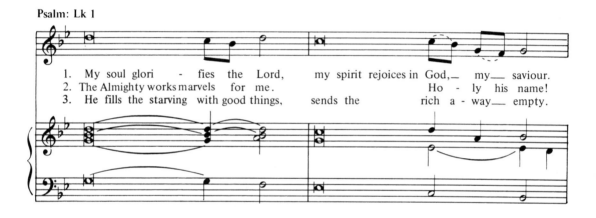

1. My soul glori - fies the Lord,    my spirit rejoices in God,__ my__ saviour.
2. The Almighty works marvels for me.              Ho - ly his name!
3. He fills the starving with good things,   sends the     rich a - way__ empty.

1. He looks on his servant in her noth - ing-ness;   henceforth all ages will call me blessed. ℟.
2. His mercy       is from age to age    on         those who fear him.℟.
3. He protects Is - rael his ser - vant,   remem - b'ring his mercy   ℟.

## 4TH SUNDAY OF ADVENT, YEAR B
*See 13th Sunday of the Year, Year A, p.80.*

# 1ST SUNDAY OF LENT, YEAR B
## 3rd Sunday of the Year, Year B   1st Sunday of Advent, Year C

**Response, 1 Lent B**                           GEOFFREY BOULTON SMITH

Your ways, Lord, are faith - ful-ness and love for those who keep your co-ve - nant.

**Response, 3 Year B**     GEOFFREY BOULTON SMITH

Lord, make me know your ways.

**Response, 1 Advent C**     STEPHEN DEAN

To you, O Lord, I lift up my soul.

**Psalm-Tone**     STEPHEN DEAN

**Ps 24**

1. Lord, make me know your | ways.
   Lord, teach me your | paths.
   Make me walk in your truth, and | teach me:
   for you are | God my | saviour.  R.

2. The Lord is good and | upright.
   He shows the path to those who | stray,
   he guides the humble in the | right path;
   he teaches his | way to the | poor.  R.

*1 Lent B and 3 Year B only*

1a. Remember your mercy, | Lord,
    and the love you have shown from of | old.
    In your love re|member me,
    because of your | goodness, O | Lord.  R.

*1 Advent C only*

3. His ways are faithfulness and | love
   for those who keep his covenant and | will.
   The Lord's friendship is for those who re|vere him;
   to them he re|veals his | covenant.  R.

# 2ND SUNDAY OF LENT, YEAR B
## 1st SETTING

**Response**

DENIS McCARTHY

I will walk in the pre-sence of the Lord in the land of the liv-ing.

**Psalm-Tone**

LAURENCE BÉVENOT

**Ps 115**

1. I trusted, even | when I | said:
   'I am sore|ly af|flicted.'
   O precious in the eyes | of the | Lord
   is the death | of his | faithful. ℟.

2. Your servant, Lord, your ser|vant am | I;
   you have loos|ened my | bonds.
   A thanksgiving sacri|fice I | make:
   I will call | on the | Lord's name. ℟.

3. My vows to the Lord I | will ful|fil
   before | all his | people,
   in the courts of the house | of the | Lord,
   in your midst, | O Je|rusalem. ℟.

## 2nd SETTING

**Response**

GEOFFREY BOULTON SMITH

I will walk in the presence of the Lord in the land of the liv-ing.

*\* Throughout, guitar chords (capo 1 fret) are an alternative to the organ accompaniment. Some guitarists
will prefer to leave off the capo and play the chords a semitone higher — F, Gm7, etc.*

**Psalm 115**

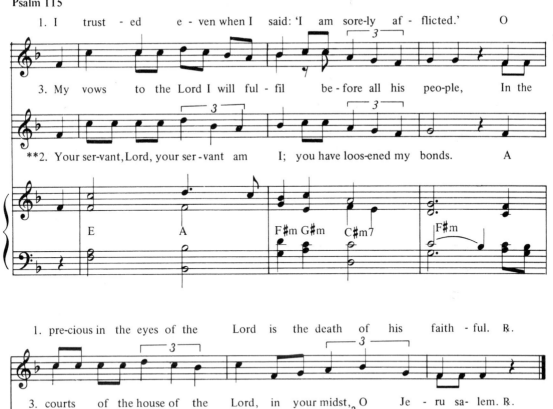

\*\**Some minor modifications in rhythm should be made by the organist in v. 2, following the rhythm of the cantor(s).*

# 3RD SUNDAY OF LENT, YEAR B
## 3rd Sunday of the Year, Year C
## Easter Vigil 6th Psalm

### 1st SETTING

**Response, 3 Lent B**                                    GEOFFREY BOULTON SMITH

You, Lord, have the mes-sage of e - ter - nal life.

**Response, 3 Year C**

Your words are spi - rit, Lord, and they are life.

**Response, Easter Vigil 6**

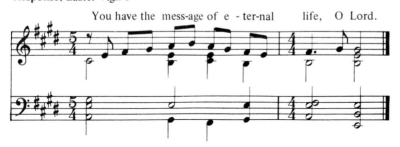

You have the mess-age of e - ter-nal life, O Lord.

**Psalm 18**

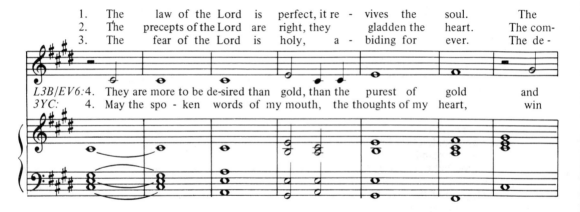

1. The law of the Lord is perfect, it re - vives the soul. The
2. The precepts of the Lord are right, they gladden the heart. The com-
3. The fear of the Lord is holy, a - biding for ever. The de-

L3B/EV6:4. They are more to be de-sired than gold, than the purest of gold and
3YC:   4. May the spo - ken words of my mouth, the thoughts of my heart, win

2nd SETTING *(not Easter Vigil)*

**Response, 3 Lent B**                              GEOFFREY BOULTON SMITH

You, Lord, have the mes - sage of e - ter - nal life.

**Response, 3 Year C**                              DENIS McCARTHY

Your words and spi - rit, Lord, and they are life.

**Psalm-Tone**                                       LAURENCE BÉVENOT

**Ps 18**

1. The law of the | Lord is perfect,
   it re|vives the | soul.
   The rule of the Lord is | to be | trusted,
   it gives wisdom | to the | simple.  ℞.

2. The precepts of the | Lord are | right,
   they glad|den the | heart.
   The command of the | Lord is | clear,
   it gives light | to the | eyes.  ℞.

3. The fear of the | Lord is | holy,
   abi|ding for | ever.
   The decrees of the | Lord are | truth
   and all | of them | just.  ℞.

4. *3 Lent B only*

   They are more to be de|sired than | gold,
   than the pur|est of | gold
   and sweeter are | they than | honey,
   than honey | from the | comb.  ℞.

4. *3 Year C only*

   May the spoken words | of my | mouth,
   the thoughts | of my | heart,
   win favour in your | sight, O | Lord,
   my rescu|er, my | rock!  ℞.

# 4TH SUNDAY OF LENT, YEAR B

**Response**

JULIA ROWNTREE

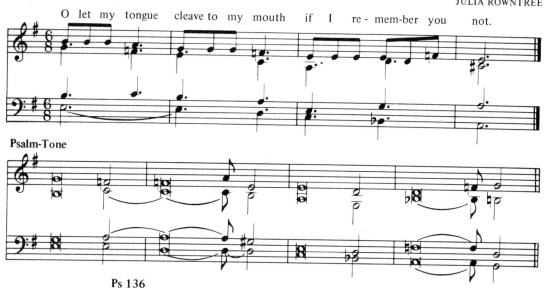

O let my tongue cleave to my mouth if I re-mem-ber you not.

**Psalm-Tone**

Ps 136

1.  By the rivers of Babylon there we sat and | wept,
    remember|ing | Zion;
    on the poplars that | grew there
    we hung up | our | harps. ℟.

2.  For it was there that they asked us, our captors, for | songs,
    our oppressors, | for | joy.
    'Sing to us,' they | said,
    'one of Zi|on's | songs.' ℟.

3.  O how could we sing the song of the | Lord
    on a|lien | soil?
    If I forget you, Je|rusalem,
    let my right | hand | wither! ℟.

4.  O let my tongue cleave to my | mouth
    if I remember | you | not,
    if I prize not Je|rusalem
    above all | my | joys! ℟.

# 5TH SUNDAY OF LENT, YEAR B
## Easter Vigil 7th Psalm, alternative

**Response**      1st SETTING    GEOFFREY BOULTON SMITH

A pure heart cre - ate for me, O God.

**Psalm-Tone**

JOSEPH GELINEAU

**Ps 50**

*1.   5 Lent B only*
Have mércy on me, Gód, in your kíndness.
In your compássion blot óut my offénce.
O wásh me more and móre from my guílt
and cléanse me fróm my sín.   ℟.

2.   A púre heart creáte for me, O Gód,
     put a stéadfast spírit withín me.
     Do not cást me awáy from your présence,
     nor depríve me of your hóly spírit.   ℟.

3.   Give me agáin the jóy of your hélp;
     with a spírit of férvour sustáin me,
     that I may téach transgréssors your wáys
     and sínners may retúrn to yóu.   ℟.

*4.   Easter Vigil 7b only*
For in sácrifice you táke no delíght,
burnt óffering from mé you would refúse,
my sacrífice, a contríte spírit.
A húmbled, contrite héart you will • not spúrn.   ℟.

## 2nd SETTING

**Response**                                        TONY BARR

A   pure - heart cre-ate   for   me,   O   God.

**Psalm-Tone**

## 2ND SUNDAY OF EASTER, YEAR B
*See 2nd Sunday of Easter, p.54.*

## 3RD SUNDAY OF EASTER, YEAR B

### 1st SETTING

**Response**                                                    JAMES WALSH

Lift up the light of your face on us, O Lord.

**Alternative Response**

Al - le - lu - ia, al - le - lu - ia!

**Psalm-Tone**

Ps 4

1.  When I call, answer me, O | God of | justice;
    from anguish you released me, have | mercy and | hear me!   R.

2.  It is the Lord who grants favours to those | whom he | loves;
    the Lord hears me when|ever I | call him.   R.

3.  'What can bring us happiness?' | many | say.
    Lift up the light of your | face on • us, O | Lord.   R.

4.  I will lie down in peace and sleep | comes at | once,
    for you alone, Lord, make me | dwell in | safety.   R.

## 2nd SETTING

**Response**                                               CHRISTOPHER WALKER

Lift up the light of your face on us, O Lord.

$\downarrow$ = c. 60

**Psalm 4**

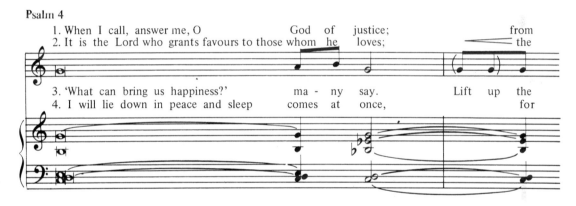

1. When I call, answer me, O God of justice; from
2. It is the Lord who grants favours to those whom he loves; the
3. 'What can bring us happiness?' ma - ny say. Lift up the
4. I will lie down in peace and sleep comes at once, for

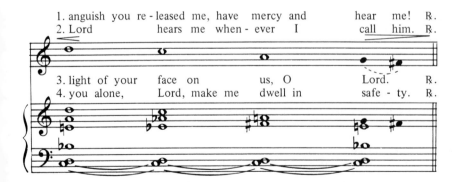

1. anguish you re - leased me, have mercy and hear me! ℞.
2. Lord hears me when - ever I call him. ℞.
3. light of your face on us, O Lord. ℞.
4. you alone, Lord, make me dwell in safe - ty. ℞.

# 4TH SUNDAY OF EASTER, YEAR B

**Response**                                                      LAURENCE BÉVENOT

**Ps 117**

1. Alleluia!
   Give thanks to the Lord for | he is | good,
   for his love | has no | end.
   It is better to take | refuge • in the | Lord
   than to | trust in | men:
   it is better to take refuge | in the | Lord
   than to | trust in | princes.  R.

2. I will thank you for you have | given | answer
   and you | are my | saviour.
   The stone which the | builders re|jected
   has be|come the | cornerstone.
   This is the work | of the | Lord,
   a marvel | in our | eyes.  R.

3. Blessed in the name of the Lord is | he who | comes.
   We bless you from the house | of the | Lord;
   I will thank you for | you have • given | answer
   and you | are my | saviour.
   Give thanks to the Lord for | he is | good;
   for his love | has no end.  R.

# 5TH SUNDAY OF EASTER, YEAR B

**Response**              1st SETTING              JAMES WALSH

**Alternative Response**

**Psalm-Tone**

**Ps 21**

1. My vows I will pay before | those who | fear him.
   The poor shall eat and shall | have their | fill.
   They shall praise the Lord, | those who | seek him.
   May their hearts live for e|ver and | ever!   ℟.

2. All the earth shall remember and return | to the | Lord,
   all families of the nations wor|ship be|fore him.     .
   They shall worship him, all the mighty | of the | earth;
   before him shall bow all who go down | to the | dust.   ℟.

3. And my soul shall live for him, my | children | serve him.
   They shall tell of the Lord to generations | yet to | come,
   declare his faithfulness to peoples | yet un|born:
   'These things the | Lord has | done.'   ℟.

2nd SETTING

**Response**

GEOFFREY BOULTON SMITH

**Psalm-Tone**

# 6TH SUNDAY OF EASTER, YEAR B
## Christmas Day

**Response**                                                          PETER SMEDLEY

**Alternative Response for Christmas Day**

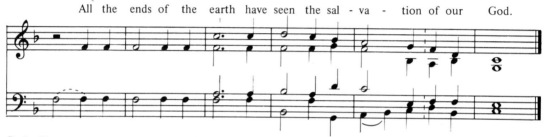

**Psalm-Tone**

**Ps 97**

1. Sing a new song to the | Lord
   for he has worked | wonders.
   His right hand and his holy | arm
   have brought | sal|vation.   ℟.

2. The Lord has made known his sal|vation;
   has shown his justice to the | nations.
   He has remembered his truth and | love
   for the house | of | Israel.   ℟.

3. All the ends of the earth have | seen
   the salvation of our | God.
   Shout to the Lord all the | earth,
   ring out your joy.   ℟.

4. *(Christmas Day only)*
   Sing psalms to the Lord with the | harp,
   with the sound of | music.
   With trumpets and the sound of the | horn
   acclaim the King, | the | Lord.   ℟.

*An alternative setting will be found on p.20.*

# 7TH SUNDAY OF EASTER, YEAR B
## 1st SETTING

GEOFFREY BOULTON SMITH

**Response**      **Alternative Response**

**Psalm-Tone**

JOSEPH GELINEAU (arr. G.B.S.)

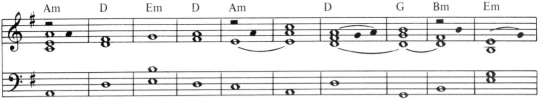

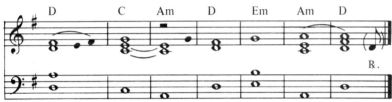

**Ps 102**

1. My sóul, give thánks | to the | Lórd,
   all my béing, | bléss his • holy | náme.
   My sóul, give | thánks to the | Lórd
   and | néver for|gét all his | bléssings. ℞.

2. For as the héavens are hígh a|bove the | éarth
   so stróng is his | lóve for • those who | féar him.
   As fár as • the | éast is • from the | wést
   so | fár does he re|móve our | síns. ℞.

3. The Lórd has set his | swáy in | héaven
   and his kíngdom is | rúling • over | áll.
   Give thánks to • the | Lórd, all his | ángels,
   mighty in | pówer, ful|fílling his | wórd. ℞.

**Response**      **2nd SETTING**      STEPHEN DEAN

**Psalm-Tone**

# TRINITY SUNDAY, YEAR B
## 19th Sunday of the Year, Year C

**Response**                  CHRISTOPHER McCURRY

Hap - py are the peo - ple the Lord has chosen as his own.

**Psalm-Tone**

Ps 32

*Trinity Year B only*

1. The word of the | Lord is | faithful
   and all his works | to be | trusted.
   The Lord loves jus|tice and | right
   and fills the earth | with his | love. ℟.

1a. By his word the | heavens were | made,
   by the breath of his mouth | all the | stars.
   He spoke; and they | came to | be.
   He commanded; they sprang | into | being. ℟.

*19th Sunday Year C only*

1. Ring out your joy to the Lord, | O you | just;
   for praise is fitting for | loyal | hearts.
   They are happy, whose God | is the | Lord,
   the people he has chosen | as his | own. ℟.

2. The Lord looks on those | who re|vere him,
   on those who hope | in his | love,
   to rescue their | souls from | death,
   to keep them a|live in | famine. ℟.

3. Our soul is waiting | for the | Lord.
   The Lord is our help | and our | shield.
   May your love be upon | us, O | Lord,
   as we place all our | hope in | you. ℟.

*An alternative setting for Trinity, Year B, will be found on p.34.*

# CORPUS CHRISTI, YEAR B

**Response**                                                        STEPHEN DEAN

The cup of sal - va - tion I will raise; I will call on the Lord's name.

**Psalm-Tone**

℞. The cup of sal-

**Ps 115**

1. How can I re|pay the | Lord
   for his | goodness to | me?
   The cup of sal|vation • I will | raise;
   I will | call on the | Lord's | name.   ℞.

2. O precious in the eyes | of the | Lord
   is the | death of his | faithful.
   Your servant, Lord, your | servant am | I;
   you have | loosened | my | bonds.   ℞.

3. A thanksgiving sacri|fice I | make:
   I will call | on the Lord's | name.
   My vows to the | Lord I • will ful|fil
   be|fore all | his | people.   ℞.

*The psalm-tone will also be found set out in full for Maundy Thursday, p.46.*


## 2ND SUNDAY OF THE YEAR, YEAR B
*See 2nd Sunday of the Year, Year A, p.69.*

## 3RD SUNDAY OF THE YEAR, YEAR B
*See 1st Sunday of Lent, Year B, p.109.*

## 4TH SUNDAY OF THE YEAR, YEAR B
*See 3rd Sunday of Lent, Year A, p.36.*

## 5TH SUNDAY OF THE YEAR, YEAR B

**Response**             GEOFFREY BOULTON SMITH

Praise the Lord who heals the broken-hearted.

**Psalm-Tone**

v.2 only

**Ps 146**

1.  Alle|lu|ia!
    Praise the Lord for | he is | good;
    sing to our God for | he is | loving:
    to him our | praise is | due.  R.

2.  The Lord builds up | Je|rusalem
    and brings back | Israel's | exiles,
    he heals the | broken-|hearted,
    he binds up | all their | wounds.
    He fixes the number | of the | stars;
    he calls each one | by its | name.  R.

3.  Our Lord is great | and | mighty;
    his wisdom can ne|ver be | measured.
    The Lord rai|ses the | lowly;
    he humbles the wicked | to the | dust.  R.

## 6TH SUNDAY OF THE YEAR, YEAR B
### 11th Sunday of the Year, Year C

**Response 6 Year B**          CHRISTOPHER WALKER

You are my hid-ing place, O   Lord;   you sur-

- round     me   with     cries     of   de - liv - er - ance.

**Response, 11 Year C**

For - give, Lord, the guilt   of   my   sin.          sin.

**Psalm-Tone**

omit in v.2b          6 Year B only          11 Year C only

omit in v.2b

**Ps 31**

1. Happy the man whose offence is | for|given,
   whose sin is | re|mitted.
   O happy the man to whom the Lord im|putes no | guilt,
   in whose spirit is | no | guile.   R̸.

2. But now I have acknowledged | my | sins;
   my guilt I did | not | hide.
   I said: 'I will confess my of|fence to the | Lord.'
   And you, Lord, have forgiven the guilt of | my | sin.   R̸.


*11th Sunday Year C only*

2b. You are my hiding place, | O | Lord;
    you save me from | dis|tress.
    you surround me with cries of | de|liverance.   R̸.

3. Rejoice, rejoice in | the | Lord,
   exult, | you | just!
   O come, ring | out your | joy,
   all you upright | of | heart.   R̸.

# 7TH SUNDAY OF THE YEAR, YEAR B

**Response**            1st SETTING            PAUL INWOOD

Heal my soul for I have sinned a - gainst you.

**Psalm 40**

1. Happy the man who considers the poor and the weak. The Lord will save him in the day of evil,

will guard him, give him life, make him happy in the land, and will not give him up to the will of his foes. ℟.

2. The Lord will help him on his bed of pain, he will bring him back from sickness to health. As for me,

I said: 'Lord, have mer-cy on me, heal my soul for I have sinned a - gainst you'. ℟.

3. If you uphold me I shall be un - harmed and set in your presence for e - ver -more. Blessed be

the Lord, the God of Is-rael     from age to age. A - men. A - men. ℟.

**Response**     2nd SETTING     CHRISTOPHER McCURRY

Heal   my   soul_____   for   I   have   sinned_ a - gainst   you._____

**Psalm 40**

1. Happy the man who considers the poor and   the   weak.   The Lord will save him in the
2. The Lord will help him on his   bed   of   pain,   he will bring him back from sick -
3. If you uphold me I shall   be   un - harmed   and set in your presence for

1. day   of   evil,   will guard him, give him life, make him happy in   the   land   and
2. -ness to health.   As for me, I said: 'Lord, have mer   -   cy   on   me, heal   my
3. e - ver - more.   Blessed be the Lord, the   God   of   Israel   from

1. will not give him   up to the will   of   his   foes. ℟.
2. soul for I have   sinned   a - gainst you.' ℟.
3. age to age. A   men.   A - men.   ℟.

## 8TH SUNDAY OF THE YEAR, YEAR B
*See 7th Sunday of the Year, Year A, p.73.*

## 9TH SUNDAY OF THE YEAR, YEAR B

**Response**                        GEOFFREY BOULTON SMITH

**Psalm-Tone**                        JOSEPH GELINEAU (adapted)

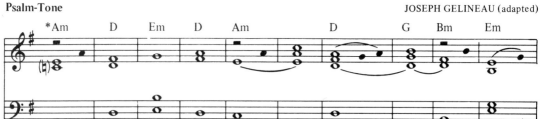

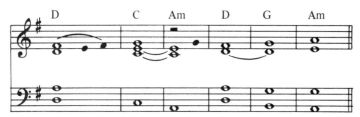

*\*Throughout, guitar-chords are an alternative to the organ accompaniment.*

**Ps 80**

1. Raise a sóng and sóund the tímbrel,
   the swéet-sounding hárp and the lúte,
   blow the trúmpet át the new móon,
   when the móon is fúll, on our féast. R̸.

2. For thís is Ísrael's láw,
   a commánd of the Gód of Jácob.
   He impósed it as • a rúle on Jóseph,
   when he went óut against the lánd of Égypt. R̸.

3. A vóice I did not knów said to mé:
   'I fréed your shóulder • from the búrden;
   your hánds were fréed from the lóad.
   You cálled in distréss and I sáved you. R̸.

4. 'Let there be nó foreign gód amóng you,
   no wórship of an álien gód.
   I am • the Lórd your Gód,
   who bróught you from the lánd of Égypt.' R̸.

## 10TH SUNDAY OF THE YEAR, YEAR B
*See 5th Sunday of Lent, Year A, p.43.*

## 11TH SUNDAY OF THE YEAR, YEAR B
### 8th Sunday of the Year, Year C

**Response**                        GEOFFREY BOULTON SMITH

Psalm-Tone    vv.1 & 3 only    v.3 only

**Ps 91**

1.  It is good to give thanks | to the | Lord,
    to make music to your name, | O Most | High,
    to proclaim your love | in the | morning
    and your truth in the watches | of the | night.  ℞.

2.  The just will flourish | like the | palm-tree
    and grow like a Le|banon | cedar.  ℞.

3.  Planted in the house | of the | Lord
    they will flourish in the courts | of our | God,
    still bearing fruit when | they are | old,
    still full of sap, | still | green,
    to proclaim that the | Lord is | just.
    In him, my rock, there | is no | wrong.  ℞.

## 12TH SUNDAY OF THE YEAR, YEAR B

1st SETTING

GEOFFREY BOULTON SMITH

Response

O give thanks to the Lord, for his love en - dures for e - ver.

Psalm-Tone                                LAURENCE BÉVENOT

**Ps 106**

1.  Some sailed to the | sea in | ships
    to trade on the | mighty | waters.
    These men have | seen the | Lord's deeds,
    the wonders he does | in the | deep.  ℞.

2.  For he spoke; he sum|moned the | gale,
    tossing the waves | of the | sea
    up to heaven and back in|to the | deep;
    their soul melted away in | their dis|tress.  ℞.

3.  Then they cried to the Lord | in their | need
    and he rescued them from | their dis|tress.
    He stilled the storm | to a | whisper:
    all the waves of the | sea were | hushed.  ℞.

4.  They rejoiced because | of the | calm
    and he led them to the haven | they de|sired.
    Let them thank the Lord | for his | love,
    the wonders he | does for | men.  ℞.

2nd SETTING

**Response**

PAUL INWOOD

♩. = 58 throughout

R. O give thanks to the Lord, for his love endures for ever. O give

**Psalm 106**

e - ver.— 1. Some sailed to the sea— in ships to trade on the might-y

waters.— These men— have seen the Lord's deeds, the won-ders he does in the

deep. R. O give thanks to the Lord, for his love endures for e-ver.—

*Last time only*

To vv. 2·4

e-ver. 2. For he spoke; he summoned the gale, — tossing the waves of the

3. Then they cried to the Lord in their need — and he res-cued them from their dis-

4. They re-joiced be-cause of the calm — and he led them to the haven they de-

2. sea — up to heaven and back into the deep; their soul melt-ed a-way in their distress ℞. O give

3.-tress. — He stilled the storm to a whis-per:— all the waves of the sea — were hushed.℞. O give

4.-sired. Let them thank the Lord for his love, — the wonders he does for men. ℞. O give

# 13TH SUNDAY OF THE YEAR, YEAR B
## 3rd Sunday of Easter, Year C
## 10th Sunday of the Year, Year C        Easter Vigil 4th Psalm

**Response**        1st SETTING        LAURENCE BÉVENOT

**Alternative harmonisation**

**Psalm-Tone**

**Ps 29**

1. I will práise you, Lórd, you have | réscued | me
and have nót let my énemies rejóice | over | me.
O Lórd, you have ráised my sóul | from the | déad,
restóred me to lífe from those who sínk in|to the | gráve.   ℟.

2. Sing psálms to the Lórd, | you who | lóve him,
give thánks to his | hóly | náme.
Hís anger lásts but a móment; his fá|vour through | lífe.
At níght there are téars, but jóy | comes with | dáwn.   ℟.

3. The Lórd lístened | and had | pity.
The Lórd cáme | to my | hélp.
For mé you have chánged my móurning | into | dáncing,
O Lórd my Gód, I will thánk | you for | éver.   ℟.

**Response**        2nd SETTING        BILL TAMBLYN

**Psalm-Tone**

## 14TH SUNDAY OF THE YEAR, YEAR B

**Response**

MOUNT ST BERNARD

Our eyes are on the Lord till he show us his mer - cy.

**Psalm-Tone**

**Ps 122**

1. To you have I lifted | up my | eyes,
   you who dwell | in the | heavens:
   my eyes, like the | eyes of | slaves
   on the hands | of their | lords. ℟.

2. Like the eyes | of a | servant
   on the hand | of her | mistress,
   so our eyes are on the | Lord our | God
   till he show | us his | mercy. ℟.

3. Have mercy on us, | Lord, have | mercy.
   We are filled | with con|tempt.
   Indeed all too full is our soul with the scorn | of the | rich,
   with the proud | man's dis|dain. ℟.

## 15TH SUNDAY OF THE YEAR, YEAR B
*See 19th Sunday of the Year, Year A, p.88.*

## 16TH SUNDAY OF THE YEAR, YEAR B
*See 4th Sunday of Lent, Year A, p.40.*

## 17TH SUNDAY OF THE YEAR, YEAR B
*See 18th Sunday of the Year, Year A, p.88.*

# 18TH SUNDAY OF THE YEAR, YEAR B

## 1st SETTING

**Response**

HAROLD BARKER

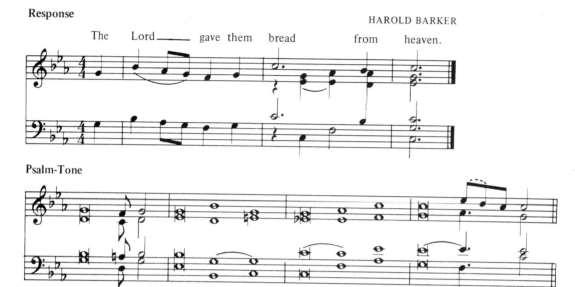

**Psalm-Tone**

Ps 77

1.  The things we have heard and | under|stood,
    the things our fáthers have tóld us,
    we will tell to the néxt generátion:
    the glories of the | Lord and his | might.   R.

2.  He commanded the | clouds a|bove
    and opened the gátes of héaven.
    He rained down mánna for their fóod,
    and gave them | bread from | heaven.   R.

3.  Mere men ate the bread | of | angels.
    He sent them abúndance of fóod.
    He brought them to his hóly lánd,
    to the mountain which his | right hand had | won.   R.

Response          2nd SETTING          TONY BARR

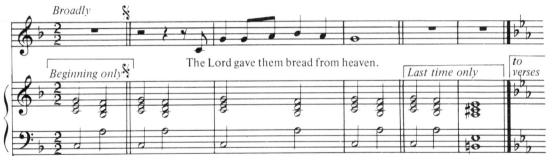

The Lord gave them bread from heaven.

*Beginning only*      *Last time only*      *to verses*

**Psalm 77**

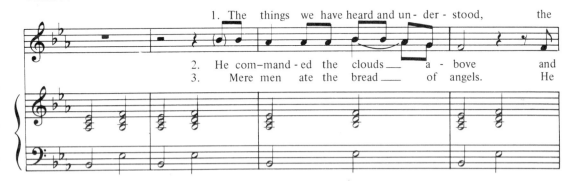

1. The things we have heard and un - der - stood, the
2. He com—mand - ed the clouds___ a - bove and
3. Mere men ate the bread___ of angels. He

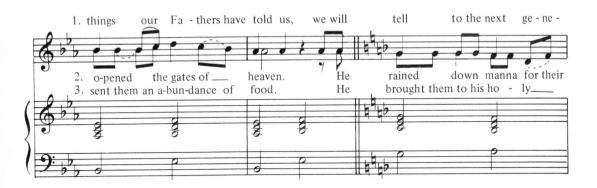

1. things our Fa - thers have told us, we will tell to the next ge - ne -
2. o-pened the gates of ___ heaven. He rained down manna for their
3. sent them an a-bun-dance of food. He brought them to his ho - ly___

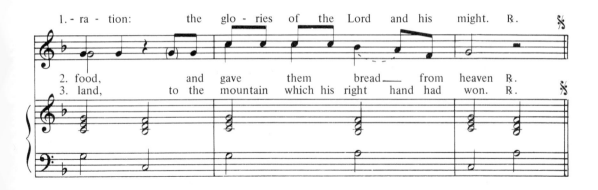

1. - ra - tion: the glo - ries of the Lord and his might. R.
2. food, and gave them bread___ from heaven R.
3. land, to the mountain which his right hand had won. R.

# 19TH SUNDAY OF THE YEAR, YEAR B
## 20th Sunday of the Year, Year B
### 21st Sunday of the Year, Year B          4th Sunday of Lent, Year C
1st SETTING

Response                                                    LAURENCE BÉVENOT

Psalm-Tone                                                  JOSEPH GELINEAU

### Ps 33

*19 Year B and 4 Lent C only*

1.  I will bléss the | Lórd at áll | times,
    his práise álways on | my | líps;
    in the Lórd my sóul shall | make its | bóast.
    The húmble shall | héar and be | glád.   ℞.

2.  Glórify | the Lórd with | mé.
    Togéther let us práise | his | náme.
    I sóught the Lórd | and he | ánswered me;
    from all my térrors | he sét me | frée.   ℞.

3.  Lóok towards | hím and be | rádiant;
    let your fáces nót be | a|báshed.
    Thís poor man cálled; | the Lord | héard him
    and réscued him from | áll his dis|tréss.   ℞.

4.  *(19 Year B only)*

The ángel of the | Lórd is en|cámped
around thóse who revére him, | to | réscue them.
Taste and sée that the | Lórd is | góod.
He is háppy who seeks | réfuge in | hím.   ℞.

*20 Year B only*

1.  I will bléss the | Lórd at áll | times,
    his práise álways on | my | líps;
    in the Lórd my sóul shall | make its | bóast.
    The húmble shall | héar and be | glád.   ℞.

2.  Revére the | Lórd, you his | sáints.
    They lack nóthing, thóse who | re|vére him.
    Stróng lions suffer wánt | and go | húngry
    but thóse who seek the | Lórd lack no |
                                      bléssing.   ℞.

3.  Cóme, | chíldren, and | héar me
    that I may téach you the féar of | the | Lórd.
    Whó is he who | lóngs for | lífe
    and many dáys, to en|jóy his pros|périty?   ℞.

4.  Then kéep | your tóngue from | évil
    and your líps from spéaking | de|céit.
    Túrn aside from évil | and do | góod;
    séek and | stríve after | péace.   ℞.

*21 Year B only*

1. I will bléss the | Lórd at áll | times,
   his práise álways on | my | líps;
   in the Lórd my sóul shall | make its | bóast.
   The húmble shall | héar and be | glád.   ℟.

2. The Lórd turns his fáce | against the | wícked
   to destróy their remémbrance from | the | éarth.
   The Lórd turns his éyes | to the | júst
   and his éars | to théir ap|péal.   ℟.

3. They | cáll and the | Lórd héars
   and réscues them in áll their | dis|tréss.
   The Lord is clóse to the | bróken-|héarted;
   those whose spírit is | crúshed he will | sáve.   ℟.

4. Mány are the | tríals of the | júst man
   but from them áll the Lórd | will | réscue him.
   He will keep gúard over | áll his | bónes,
   not óne of his | bónes shall be | bróken.

5. Évil brings | déath to the | wícked;
   those who háte the góod | are | dóomed.
   The Lord ránsoms the sóuls | of his | sérvants.
   Those who híde in him shall | nót be con|démned.   ℟.

## 2nd SETTING

Optional instrumental descant

PAUL INWOOD

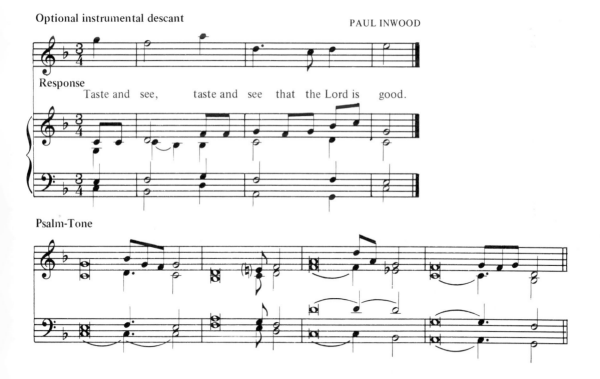

Response

Taste and see,     taste and see   that   the Lord is     good.

Psalm-Tone

## 22ND SUNDAY OF THE YEAR, YEAR B
### 16th Sunday of the Year, Year C

**Response**                                                     CHRISTOPHER WALKER

Lord, who shall be ad-mit-ted___ to your tent?

**Psalm-Tone**

*Omit v.3 16Y/C*                                              *16 Y/C, v.1, only*

**Ps 14**

1. *(22 Year B only)*
Lord, who shall dwell on your | holy | mountain?
He who walks with|out | fault:
he who | acts with | justice
and speaks the truth from | his | heart.    ℟.

1. *(16 Year C only)*
Lord, who shall dwell on your | holy | mountain?
He who walks with|out | fault;
he who | acts with | justice
and speaks the truth from | his | heart;
he who does not slander with | his | tongue.    ℟.

2. He who does no | wrong to • his | brother,
who casts no slur on | his | neighbour,
who holds the godless | in dis|dain,
but honours those who fear | the | Lord.    ℟.

3. *(22 Year B only)*
He who keeps his pledge, | come what | may;
who takes no interest on | a | loan
and accepts no bribes a|gainst the | innocent.
Such a man will stand | firm for | ever.    ℟.

3. *(16 Year C only)*
He takes no interest on | a | loan
and accepts no bribes a|gainst the | innocent.
Such a man will stand | firm for | ever.    ℟.

*Another setting will be found on p.170.*

## 23RD SUNDAY OF THE YEAR, YEAR B

### 32nd Sunday of the Year, Year B       26th Sunday of the Year, Year C

Response                                   1st SETTING                          STEPHEN DEAN

**Ps 145**

1. It is the Lórd who keeps fáith for éver,
   who is júst to thóse who are oppréssed.
   It is hé who gives bréad to the húngry,
   the Lórd, who sets prísoners frée.   ℟.

2. It is the Lórd who gives síght to the blínd,
   who ráises up thóse who are bowed dówn.
   It is the Lórd who lóves the júst,
   the Lórd who protécts the stránger.   ℟.

3. The Lórd upholds the wídow and órphan,
   but thwárts the páth of the wícked.
   The Lórd will réign for éver,
   Zion's Gód, from áge to áge.   ℟.

*23rd Sunday of Year B*

2nd SETTING

**Response**

MICHAEL DAWNEY

*Note: the Lectionary contains a number of variants in the editing of the text of this psalm.*
*The correct text for all three Sundays is as given above.*

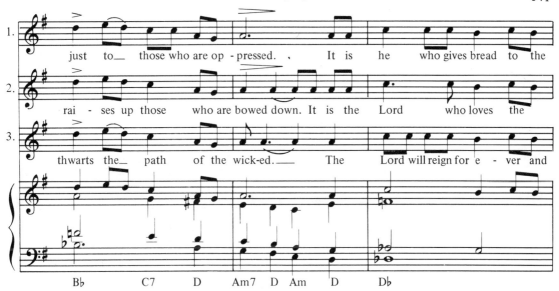

1. just to— those who are op - pressed. It is he who gives bread to the
2. rai - ses up those who are bowed down. It is the Lord who loves the
3. thwarts the— path of the wick-ed.— The Lord will reign for e - ver and

Bb    C7    D    Am7    D    Am    D    Db

1. hun - gry, the Lord, who sets pri - son - ers free. ℞. My
2. just, the Lord who pro-tects the— stran-ger. ℞. My
3. e - ver, Zion's God, from— age to— age. ℞. My

C    Bm    Am    Bm    Em7    D

## 24TH SUNDAY OF THE YEAR, YEAR B

**Response**                                                    DENIS McCARTHY

**Psalm-Tone**                                                LAURENCE BÉVENOT

Ps 114

1. Alleluia! I love the Lord for | he has | heard
   the cry of | my ap|peal;
   for he turned his | ear to | me
   in the day | when I | called him.  ℟.

2. They surrounded me, the | snares of | death,
   with the anguish | of the | tomb;
   they caught me, sorrow | and dis|tress.
   I called on the Lord's name. O Lord my | God
                    de|liver me!  ℟.

3. How gracious is the | Lord, and | just;
   our God | has com|passion.
   The Lord protects the | simple | hearts;
   I was helpless | so he | saved me.  ℟.

4. He has kept my soul from death, my | eyes
                                    from | tears
   and my | feet from | stumbling.
   I will walk in the presence | of the | Lord
   in the land | of the | living.  ℟.

## 25TH SUNDAY OF THE YEAR, YEAR B

**Response**          LAURENCE BÉVENOT

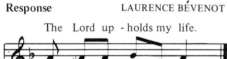

**Psalm-Tone**

Ps 53

1. O God, save me | by your | name;
   by your power, up|hold my | cause.
   O God, | hear my | prayer;
   listen to the words | of my | mouth. ℟.

2. For proud men have | risen a|gainst me,
   ruthless men | seek my | life.
   They have no re|gard for | God. ℟.

3. But I have God | for my | help.
   The Lord up|holds my | life.
   I will sacrifice to you with | willing | heart
   and praise your name for | it is | good. ℟.

# 26TH SUNDAY OF THE YEAR, YEAR B
## 1st SETTING

**Response**                                  DENIS McCARTHY

**Psalm-Tone**                               LAURENCE BÉVENOT

Ps 18

1. The law of the | Lord is | perfect,
   it re|vives the | soul.
   The rule of the Lord is | to be | trusted,
   it gives wisdom | to the | simple. ℟.

2. The fear of the | Lord is | holy,
   abid|ing for | ever.
   The decrees of the | Lord are | truth
   and all | of them | just. ℟.

3. So in them your servant | finds in|struction;
   great reward is | in their | keeping.
   But who can detect | all his | errors?
   From hidden | faults ac|quit me. ℟.

4. From presumption re|strain your | servant
   and let | it not | rule me.
   Then shall | I be | blameless,
   clean | from grave | sin. ℟.

2nd SETTING

**Response**       GEOFFREY BOULTON SMITH

**Psalm-Tone**

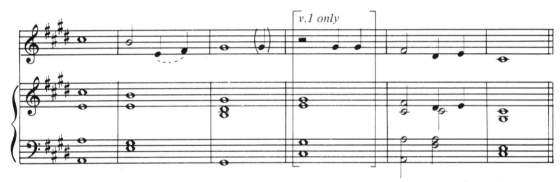

**Ps 18**

1. The láw of the Lórd is pérfect,
   it revíves the sóul.
   The rúle of the Lórd is to be trústed,
   it gives wísdom to the símple. ℟.

2. The féar of the Lórd is hóly,
   abíding for éver.
   The decrées of the Lórd are trúth
   and áll of them júst. ℟.

3. So in thém your sérvant finds instrúction;
   great rewárd is in their kéeping.
   But whó can detéct all his érrors?
   From hídden faults acquít me. ℟.

4. From presúmption restráin your sérvant
   and lét it not rúle me.
   Thén shall I be blámeless,
   cléan from grave sín. ℟.

## 27TH SUNDAY OF THE YEAR, YEAR B

**Response**      1st SETTING      PAUL JOHNSTONE

**Psalm 127**

**Verses 1 and 2**

1. O bless-ed are those who fear the Lord and walk in his ways! ___
2. Your wife like a fruit-ful vine in *omit v.2* the heart of your house; ___

___ By the la-bour of your hands you shall eat. You will be happy and pros - per. R.
___ your chil - dren like shoots of the o-live a - round your ta - ble. R.

**Verse 3**

In - deed ___ thus shall be bless - ed the man ___ who

fears the Lord. May the Lord bless you from Zi - on in a

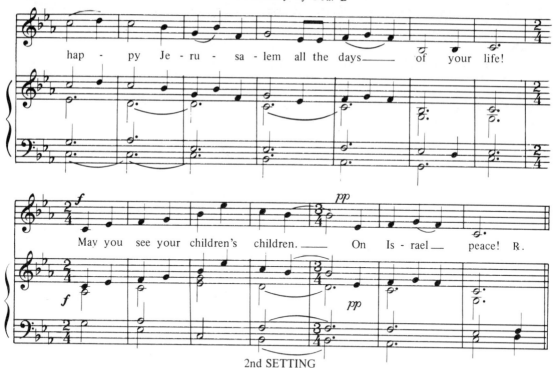

hap - py Je - ru - sa - lem all the days___ of your life!

May you see your children's children. ___ On Is - rael___ peace! ℟.

2nd SETTING

SEBASTIAN WOLFF

**Response**

May    the Lord bless___ us    all the days    of    our    life

**Psalm-Tone**

v.3 only

**Ps 127**

1. O blessed are those who | fear the | Lord
   and walk in | his | ways!
   By the labour of your hands you | shall | eat.
   You will be happy | and | prosper.  ℟.

2. *Your wife like a | fruitful | vine
   in the heart of | your | house;
   your children like shoots of | the | olive
   around | your | table.  ℟.

3. Indeed thus shall be blessed the man who | fears the | Lord.
   May the Lord bless you | from Zion
   in a happy Jerusalem all the days of | your | life!
   May you see your child|ren's | children.
   On Is |rael, |peace!  ℟.

*In the Lectionary, v. 2 begins 'Your wife will be like . . .'.

## 28TH SUNDAY OF THE YEAR, YEAR B

1st SETTING

STEPHEN DEAN

**Response**

Fill us with your love that we may re - joice.
Ps. 89
With feeling
1. Make us know the shortness of our life that we may gain wis - dom of heart.
rall.
Lord, relent! Is your anger for e-ver? show pity to your servants. ℟.
2. In the morning, fill us with your love; we shall ex - ult and re - joice all our days.
Give us joy to bal-ance our af - flic - tion for the years when we knew mis-for-tune. ℟.

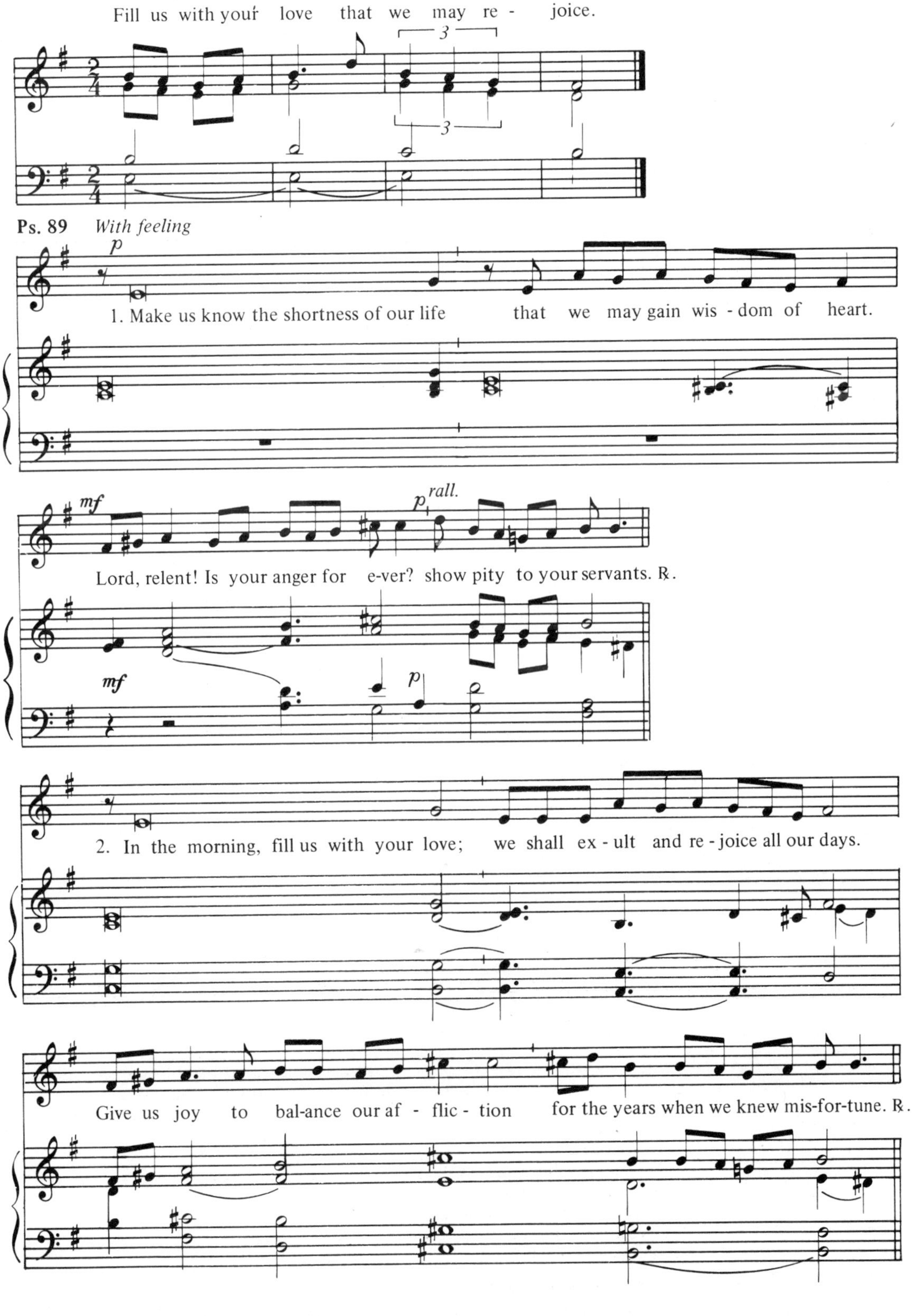

3. Show forth your work to your servants; let your glo - ry shine on their children.

Let the fa-vour of the Lord be up - on us: give suc -cess to the work of our hands. ℟.

**Alternative Psalm-Tone** *(Response as above)*                    JAMES WALSH

Ps 89

1. Make us know the shortness | of our | life
   that we may gain wis|dom of | heart.
   Lord, relent! Is your | anger for | ever?
   Show pity | to your | servants.  ℟.

2. In the morning, fill us | with your | love;
   we shall exult and rejoice | all our | days.
   Give us joy to ba|lance our af|fliction
   for the years when we | knew mis|fortune.  ℟.

3. Show forth your work | to your | servants;
   let your glory shine | on their | children.
   Let the favour of the | Lord be up|on us:
   give success to the **work** | **of our** | hands.  ℟.

2nd SETTING

BILL TAMBLYN

R. Fill us with your love that we may re-joice.

Ps 89

1. Máke us know the shórtness of our lífe
   that wé may gain wísdom of héart.
   Lord, relént! Is your ánger for éver?
   Shów píty to your sérvants. R.

2. In the mórning, fíll us with your lóve;
   we shall exúlt and rejóice all our dáys.
   Give us jóy to bálance our afflíction
   for the yéars when we knéw misfórtune. R.

3. Shów forth your wórk to your sérvants;
   let your glóry shíne on their chíldren.
   Let the fávour of the Lórd be upón us:
   give súccess to the wórk of our hánds. R.

# 29TH SUNDAY OF THE YEAR, YEAR B

*See 2nd Sunday of Lent, Year A, p.34*

# 30TH SUNDAY OF THE YEAR, YEAR B
## 2nd Sunday of Advent, Year C
## 5th Sunday of Lent, Year C

**Response**                                                    ROMUALD SIMPSON

**Psalm-Tone**

**Ps 125**

1. When the Lord delivered | Zion from | bondage,
   it seemed | like a | dream.
   Then was our mouth | filled with | laughter,
   on our lips | there were | songs.  R.

2. The heathens themselves | said: 'What | marvels
   the Lord | worked for | them!'
   What marvels the Lord | worked for | us!
   Indeed | we were | glad.  R.

3. Deliver us, O Lord, | from our | bondage
   as | streams in | dry land.
   Those who are sow|ing in | tears
   will sing | when they | reap.  R.

4. They go out, they go out, | full of | tears,
   carrying seed | for the | sowing:
   they come back, they come back, | full of | song,
   carry|ing their | sheaves.  R.

# 31ST SUNDAY OF THE YEAR, YEAR B
*See 30th Sunday of the Year, Year A, p.102.*

# 32ND SUNDAY OF THE YEAR, YEAR B
*See 23rd Sunday of the Year, Year B, p.139.*

# 33RD SUNDAY OF THE YEAR, YEAR B
## Easter Vigil 2nd Psalm

### 1st SETTING

**Response**                                    LAURENCE BÉVENOT

**Psalm-Tone**

*omit v.3*

**Ps 15**

1. O Lórd, it is yóu who are my pór|tion and | cúp;
   it is yóu yoursélf who | are my | príze.
   I kéep the Lórd éver | in my | síght:
   since hé is at my ríght hand, Í | shall stand | fírm.   ℟.

2. And so my héart rejóices, my | sóul is | glád;
   even my bódy shall | rést in | sáfety.
   For yóu will not léave my sóul a|mong the | déad,
   nor lét your belóved | knów de|cáy.   ℟.

3. Yóu will shów me the | páth of | lífe,
   the fúllness of jóy | in your | présence,
   at yóur right hánd háppi|ness for | éver.   ℟.

2nd SETTING

**Response**

BILL TAMBLYN

*Strong*
Pre - serve me,  God,___  I take ref - uge in  you.___

*Last time only*

*mf*

**Psalm-Tone**

*omit in v.3*

# LAST SUNDAY OF THE YEAR, YEAR B
## Solemnity of Christ the King

**Response**

LAURENCE BÉVENOT

The Lord is king with ma - jes - ty en - robed.

**Psalm-Tone**

Ps 92

1. The Lord is king, with maje|sty en|robed;
   the Lord has robed him|self with | might,
   he has girded him|self with | power. R.

2. The world you made firm, not | to be | moved;
   your throne has stood firm | from of | old.
   From all eternity, O | Lord, you | are. R.

3. Truly your decrees are | to be | trusted.
   Holiness is fitting | to your | house,
   O Lord, until the | end of | time. R.

# 1ST SUNDAY OF ADVENT, YEAR C

**Response**

ALAN REES

To you, O Lord, I lift up my soul.

**Psalm-Tone**

Ps 24

1.  Lórd, make me knów your wáys.
    Lord, téach mé your páths.
    Make me wálk in your trúth, and téach me:
    for yoú are Gód my sáviour.  ℟.

2.  The Lórd is góod and úpright.
    He shóws the páth to those who stráy,
    he gúides the húmble in the ríght path;
    he téaches his wáy to the póor.  ℟.

3.  His wáys are fáithfulness and lóve
    for thóse who keep his cóvenant and wíll.
    The Lord's fríendship is for thóse who revére him;
    to thém he revéals his cóvenant.  ℟.

*An alternative setting will be found on p.109.*

## 2ND SUNDAY OF ADVENT, YEAR C
*See 30th Sunday of the Year, Year B, p.150.*

## 3RD SUNDAY OF ADVENT, YEAR C
### Easter Vigil 5th Psalm

Response, 3 Advent C     1st SETTING     LAURENCE BÉVENOT

Sing and shout for joy, for  great in your midst is the  Ho-ly One of  Israel.

Response, Easter Vigil 5

With  joy  you will  draw wa-ter  from the  wells  of  sal-vat-ion.

Psalm: Is 12

1. Truly, God is my salvation,  I trust, I shall not fear.  For the Lord is my strength, my song,

1. he  became my saviour. With joy you will draw water  from the  wells  of sal-va-tion.  ℟.

2. Give thanks to the Lord, give praise to his name! Make his mighty deeds known to the peoples!
3. Sing a psalm                           to the Lord    for he has done             glo-rious deeds,

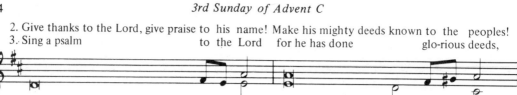

2. Declare the greatness of   his name. ℟.
3. make them known to all   the earth!    Peo-ple of Zion,        sing and shout for joy,   for

3. great      in your midst is the   Ho - ly One of  Is - rael.   ℟.

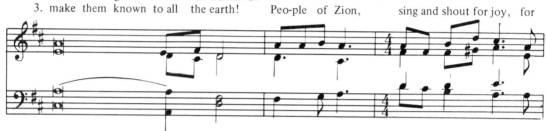

**Response**                        **2nd SETTING**                CHRISTOPHER WALKER

Sing and shout for   joy     for    great    in your  midst  is the    Ho - ly One__

__ of   Is - ra - el. __

**Psalm-Tone**

Is 12

1.  Truly, God is | my sal|vation,
    I trust, I | shall not | fear.
    For the Lord is my | strength, my | song,
    he became | my | saviour.
    With joy you | will draw | water
    from the wells of | sal|vation.   R.

2.  Give thanks to the Lord, give praise to | his | name!
    Make his mighty deeds known | to the | peoples!
    Declare the greatness of | his | name.   R.

3.  Sing a psalm | to the | Lord
    for he has done | glorious | deeds,
    make them known to | all the | earth!
    People of Zion, sing and shout | for | joy
    for great | in your | midst
    is the Holy One | of | Israel.   R.

# 4TH SUNDAY OF ADVENT, YEAR C
*See 1st Sunday of Advent, Year B, p.106.*

# 1ST SUNDAY OF LENT, YEAR C

## 1st SETTING

**Response**                                                    PETER SMEDLEY

**Psalm-Tone**

**Ps 90**

1. He who dwélls in the shélter of the | Most |Hígh
   and abídes in the sháde of the Al|míghty
   sáys to the Lórd: 'My | réfuge,
   my strónghold, my Gód in whom | I | trúst!'  ℟.

2. Upon yóu no évil | shall | fáll,
   no plágue appróach where you | dwéll.
   For yóu has he commánded his | ángels,
   to kéep you in áll | your | wáys.  ℟.

3. Théy shall bear yóu upon | their | hánds
   lest you stríke your fóot against a | stóne.
   On the líon and the víper you will | tréad
   and trámple the young líon and | the | drágon.  ℟.

4. His lóve he set on mé, so I | will | réscue him;
   protéct him for he knóws my | náme.
   When he cálls I shall ánswer: 'I am | wíth you.'
   I will sáve him in distréss and give | him | glóry.  ℟.

**Response**          2nd SETTING          BILL TAMBLYN

# 2ND SUNDAY OF LENT, YEAR C
## 3rd Sunday of the Year, Year A

**Response**                                                        PAUL INWOOD

**Psalm-Tone**

**Ps 26**   1.   The Lord is my light and | my | help;
            whom shall | I | fear?
            The Lord is the stronghold | of my | life;
            before whom shall | I | shrink?   R̥.

*3 Year A only*

2.   There is one thing I ask of | the | Lord,
     for this | I | long,
     to live in the house of | the | Lord
     all the days of | my | life,
     to savour the sweetness | of the | Lord,
     to behold | his | temple.   R̥.

*2 Lent C only*

2.   O Lord, hear my voice when | I | call;
     have mercy | and | answer.
     Of you my | heart has | spoken:
     'Seek | his | face.'   R̥.

2a.  It is your face, O Lord, that | I | seek;
     hide not | your | face.
     Dismiss not your ser|vant in | anger;
     you have been | my | help.   R̥.

3.   I am sure I shall see the | Lord's | goodness
     in the land of | the | living.
     Hope in him, hold firm | and take | heart.
     Hope in | the | Lord.   R̥.

*An alternative setting will be found on p.62.*

### 3RD SUNDAY OF LENT, YEAR C
*See 24th Sunday of the Year, Year A, p.98.*

### 4TH SUNDAY OF LENT, YEAR C
*See 19th Sunday of the Year, Year B, p.136.*

### 5TH SUNDAY OF LENT, YEAR C
*See 30th Sunday of the Year, Year B, p.150.*

### 2ND SUNDAY OF EASTER, YEAR C
*See 2nd Sunday of Easter, Year A, p.54.*

### 3RD SUNDAY OF EASTER, YEAR C
*See 13th Sunday of the Year, Year B, p.132.*

### 4TH SUNDAY OF EASTER, YEAR C
*See 11th Sunday of the Year, Year A, p.78.*

## 5TH SUNDAY OF EASTER, YEAR C

**Response**                    GEOFFREY BOULTON SMITH

I will bless your name for e - ver, O God my King.

**Psalm-Tone**                    JAMES WALSH

*omit in v.3*

**Ps 144**

1. The Lord is kind and | full of com |passion,
   slow to anger, abound|ing in | love.
   How good is the | Lord to | all,
   compassionate to | all his | creatures.  ℟.

2. All your creatures shall thank you, O Lord, and your friends shall | repeat their | blessing.
   They shall speak of the glory of your reign and declare your | might, O | God,
   to make known to men | your mighty | deeds
   and the glorious splendour | of your | reign.  ℟.

3. Yours is an e|verlasting | kingdom;
   your rule lasts from | age to | age.  ℟.

## 6TH SUNDAY OF EASTER, YEAR C
*See 20th Sunday of the Year, Year A, p.92.*

# 7TH SUNDAY OF EASTER, YEAR C
## 1st SETTING

**Response**                                          GEOFFREY BOULTON SMITH

(Al - le - lu - ia,          al - le - lu - ia!)
The Lord is    king, most high a - bove all the    earth.

**Psalm-Tone**

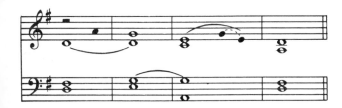

**Ps 96**

1. The Lórd is kíng, let éarth rejóice,
   the mány cóastlands be glád.
   His thróne is jústice and ríght.  ℞.

2. The skíes procláim his jústice;
   all péoples sée his glóry.
   All you spírits, wórship hím.  ℞.

3. For yóu indéed • are the Lórd
   most hígh above áll the éarth
   exálted fár a•bove all spírits.  ℞.

## 2nd SETTING

**Response**                                          PAUL JOHNSTONE

The Lord is king, the Lord is king, most high a - bove all the earth.

*Verses may be sung by: sopranos and altos; or tenors and basses; or sopranos/tenors together and altos/
basses together*

Ps 96

1. The Lord is king, let earth re-joice, the many coast-lands be glad. His

1. throne is just - ice and right. R.

2. The skies pro-claim his just - ice; all peo-ples see— his glo - ry.

2. All you spi - rits, wor-ship him. R.

3. For you in-deed __ are the Lord most high a-bove all the earth, ex-alt-

3. -ed far a-bove all spi - rits. ℞.

## TRINITY SUNDAY, YEAR C

**Response**                                                                 SEBASTIAN WOLFF

How great is your name, O Lord our __ God, through all the earth!

**Psalm-Tone**

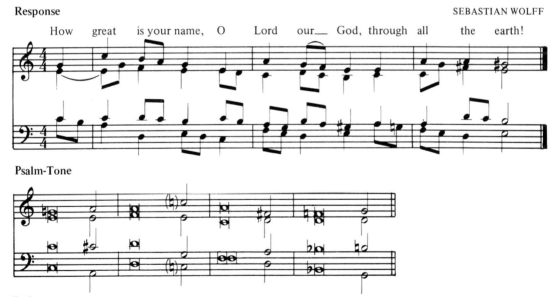

Ps 8

1. When I see the heavens, the work of your | hands,
   the moon and the stars which you ar|ranged,
   what is man that you should keep him in | mind,
   mortal man that you | care for him?  ℞.

2. Yet you have made him little less than a | god;
   with glory and honour you | crowned him,
   gave him power over the works of your | hand,
   put all things under his | feet.  ℞.

3. All of them, sheep and | cattle,
   yes, even the savage | beasts,
   birds of the air, and | fish
   that make their way through the | waters.  ℞.

# CORPUS CHRISTI, YEAR C
## (Ordinations)

CHRISTOPHER McCURRY

**Response**

*Strongly*

Capo 1st fret:

You are a priest for e - ver,      a priest like Mel-chi-ze-dek of old.

**Psalm-Tone**

*v.1 and v.3 only*

**Ps 109**

1. The Lord's revelation | to my | Master:
   'Sit | on my | right:
   I will | put your foes be|neath your | feet.'  ℟.

2. The Lord will | send from | Zion
   your sce|ptre of | power:
   rule in the midst of | all your | foes.  ℟.

3. A prince from the day | of your | birth
   on the | holy | mountains;
   from the | womb before the daybreak | I be|got you.  ℟.

4. The Lord has sworn an oath he | will not | change.
   'You are a | priest for | ever,
   a priest like Melchize|dek of | old.'  ℟.

# 2ND SUNDAY OF THE YEAR, YEAR C
## 1st SETTING

PAUL INWOOD

**Response**

*To verses*  *Last time*

Pro - claim, pro-claim the won-ders of the Lord a-mong all the peo-ples. peo-ples.

**Psalm 95**

1. O sing a new song to the Lord, sing to the Lord all the earth. [
2. Pro-claim his help day by day, tell among the na-tions his glory [
3. Give the Lord, you fami-lies of peoples, give the Lord glo - ry and power, [
4. 'Worship the Lord in his temple. O earth, trem - ble be-fore him. Pro-claim to the nations:

1. ] O sing to the Lord, bless his name. R.
2. ] and his won - ders a - mong all the peo - ples. R.
3. ] give the Lord ___ the glo - ry of his name. R.
4. 'God is king.' He will judge ___ the peo - ples in fair - ness. R.

**Response**      2nd SETTING      DENIS McCARTHY

Pro-claim the won-ders of the Lord    a - mong all the peo - ples.

**Psalm-Tone**                    LAURENCE BÉVENOT

*v.4 only*

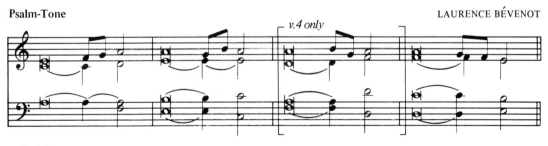

**Ps 95**

1. O sing a new song | to the | Lord,
   sing to the Lord | all the | earth.
   O sing to the Lord, | bless his | name. R.

2. Proclaim his help | day by | day,
   tell among the na|tions his | glory
   and his wonders among | all the | peoples. R.

3. Give the Lord, you fami|lies of | peoples,
   give the Lord glo|ry and | power,
   give the Lord the glory | of his | name. R.

4. Worship the Lord | in his | temple.
   O earth, trem|ble be|fore him.
   Proclaim to the nations: | 'God is | king.'
   He will judge the peo|ples in | fairness. R.

# 3RD SUNDAY OF THE YEAR, YEAR C
*See 3rd Sunday of Lent, Year B, p.112.*

## 4TH SUNDAY OF THE YEAR, YEAR C

**Response**                                  SEBASTIAN WOLFF

**Psalm-Tone**

**Ps 70**

1. In you, O Lord, | I take | refuge;
   let me never be put | to | shame.
   In your justice rescue | me, | free me:
   pay heed to me | and I save me.   ℞.

2. Be a rock where I | can take | refuge,
   a mighty stronghold | to I save me;
   for you are my rock, | my | stronghold.
   Free me from the hand of | the | wicked.   ℞.

3. It is you, O Lord, who | are my | hope,
   my trust, O Lord, since | my | youth.
   On you I have leaned from | my | birth,
   from my mother's womb you have been | my | help.   ℞.

4. My lips will tell | of your | justice
   and day by day of | your | help.
   O God, you have taught me from | my | youth
   and I proclaim your won|ders | still.   ℞.

## 5TH SUNDAY OF THE YEAR, YEAR C
### 17th Sunday of the Year, Year C
#### 1st SETTING

**Response, 5 Year C**                             DENIS McCARTHY

**Response, 17 Year C**                         DENIS McCARTHY, adapted

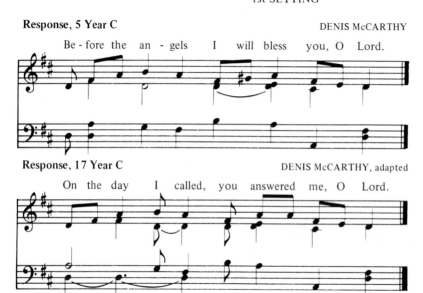

**Psalm-Tone**

LAURENCE BÉVENOT

### Ps 137

1. I thank you, Lord, with | all my | heart,
   you have heard the words | of my | mouth.
   Before the angels | I will | bless you.
   I will adore before your | holy | temple.   ℟.

2. I thank you for your faithful|ness and | love
   which excel all we | ever | knew of you.
   On the day I | called, you | answered;
   you increased the strength | of my | soul.

3. *5 Sunday Year C only*

All earth's | kings shall | thank you
when they hear the words | of your | mouth.
They shall sing | of the | Lord's ways:
'How great is the glory | of the | Lord!'   ℟.

3  *17 Sunday Year C only*

The Lord is high yet he looks | on the | lowly
and the haughty he knows | from a|far.
Though I walk in the midst | of af|fliction
you give me life and frus|trate my | foes.   ℟.

4. You stretch out your | hand and | save me,
   your hand will do all | things for | me.
   Your love, O Lord, | is e|ternal,
   discard not the work | of your | hands.   ℟.

**Response, 5 Year C**                2nd SETTING                BILL TAMBLYN

*Pastoral*
Be - fore the an - gels        I will bless you, O  Lord.

**Response, 17 Year C**

*Pastoral*
On the day I called        you an-swered me, O  Lord.

**Psalm-Tone**                                            JOSEPH GELINEAU

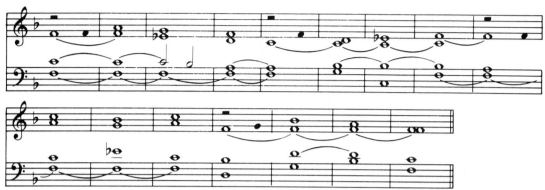

Ps 137

1. I thánk you, Lórd with all my héart,
   you have héard the wórds of my móuth.
   Befóre the ángels I will bléss you.
   I will adóre before your hóly témple.  ℞.

2. I thánk you for your fáithfulness and lóve
   which excél áll we ever knéw of you.
   On the dáy I cálled, you ánswered;
   you incréased the stréngth of my sóul.

3. *5 Sunday Year C only*

Áll earth's kíngs shall thánk you
when they héar the wórds of your móuth.
Théy shall síng of the Lórd's ways:
'How gréat is the glóry of the Lórd!'  ℞.

3. *17 Sunday Year C only*

The Lord is hígh yet he lóoks on the lówly
and the háughty he knóws from afár.
Though I wálk in the mídst of afflíction
you give me lífe and frustráte my fóes.  ℞.

4. You strétch out your hánd and sáve me,
   your hánd will do áll things for mé.
   Your lóve, O Lórd, is etérnal,
   discárd not the wórk of your hánds.  ℞.

# 6TH SUNDAY OF THE YEAR, YEAR C

**Response**                                              PAUL INWOOD

Hap-py the man who has placed his *To verses* trust in the Lord. *Last time* trust in the Lord.

(Org.)

**Psalm-Tone**

Ps 1

1. Happy indeed is the man who | follows not the counsel of the | wicked;
   nor lingers in the way of | sinners nor sits in the company of | scorners,
   but whose delight is the law of the Lord and who ponders his law | day and | night.   ℞.

2. He is like a tree that is | planted beside the flowing | waters,
   that yields its fruit in due | season and whose leaves shall never | fade;
   and all that he | does shall | prosper.   ℞.

3. Not so are the | wicked, not | so!
   For they like winnowed chaff shall be | driven away by the | wind.
   For the Lord guards the way of the just but the way of the wicked | leads to | doom.   ℞.

## 7TH SUNDAY OF THE YEAR, YEAR C
*See 7th Sunday of the Year, Year A, p.73.*

## 8TH SUNDAY OF THE YEAR, YEAR C
*See 11th Sunday of the Year, Year B, p.128.*

## 9TH SUNDAY OF THE YEAR, YEAR C
### 21st Sunday of the Year, Year C
#### 1st SETTING

**Response**            GEOFFREY BOULTON SMITH

Go out to the whole world, pro-claim the Good News.
(Al-le - lu - ia, al-e - lu - ia, al - le - lu - - ia!)

**Psalm-Tone**            JAMES WALSH

Ps 116

Alleluia! O praise the | Lord, all you | nations,
acclaim him, | all you | peoples!
Strong is his | love for | us;
he is faith|ful for | ever.   ℞.

*See notes overleaf.*

*9th Sunday of Year C*

2nd SETTING

CHRISTOPHER WALKER

Notes: *The Lectionary Response for 9 Year C is incorrect: the word 'and' should be omitted, as in the settings above. For 21 Year C, the verse is split into two halves separated by an additional response. This is not recommended. Where 'Alleluia' is used as the Response, this word should be omitted from the beginning of the verse.*

# 10TH SUNDAY OF THE YEAR, YEAR C
*See 13th Sunday of the Year, Year B, p.132.*

# 11TH SUNDAY OF THE YEAR, YEAR C
*See 6th Sunday of the Year, Year B, p.124.*

# 12TH SUNDAY OF THE YEAR, YEAR C
*See 22nd Sunday of the Year, Year A, p.95.*

# 13TH SUNDAY OF THE YEAR, YEAR C
*See 3rd Sunday of Easter, Year A, p.56.*

# 14TH SUNDAY OF THE YEAR, YEAR C
*See 6th Sunday of Easter, Year A, p.60.*

## 15TH SUNDAY OF THE YEAR, YEAR C

**Response**                                                        DENIS McCARTHY

Seek the Lord, you who are poor,____ and your hearts will re - vive.

**Psalm-Tone**                                                   LAURENCE BÉVENOT

A        B        C        D

### Ps 68

1. This is my | prayer to | you,
   my prayer | for your | favour.
   In your great love, answer | me, O | God,
   with your help that | never | fails:
   Lord, answer for your | love is | kind;            (A)
   in your compassion, | turn to|wards me.  ℟.      (D)

2. As for me in my pover|ty and | pain
   let your help, O God, | lift me | up.
   I will praise God's name | with a | song;
   I will glorify him | with thanks|giving.  ℟.

3. The poor when they see it | will be | glad
   and God-seeking hearts | will re|vive;
   for the Lord listens | to the | needy
   and does not spurn his servants | in their | chains.  ℟.

4. For God will bring | help to | Zion
   and rebuild the ci|ties of | Judah.
   The sons of his servants | shall in|herit it;
   those who love his | name shall | dwell there.  ℟.

# 16TH SUNDAY OF THE YEAR, YEAR C

BILL TAMBLYN

**Response**

Voices

R. Lord, who shall be ad - mitted to your tent?—

Organ/
Guitars
(improvise)

**Psalm 14**

1. Lord, who shall dwell on your holy mountain?——
2. [*accompaniment only* - - - - - - - - - - - - - - - - - - - - - - - - - - - - - ]
3. He who takes no interest on a loan and ac-

1. He who walks without fault; he who
2. He who does no wrong to his brother, who casts no
3.-cepts no bribes a-gainst the innocent. Such a man will stand

1. acts with— justice and speaks the truth from his
2. slur on his neighbour, who holds the godless in dis-
3. firm for— ever. (*End of v.3*) R.

1. heart; he who does not slander with his tongue. R.
2. dain, but honours those who fear the Lord. R.

*See also 22nd Sunday of the Year. Year B. p.138.*

## 17TH SUNDAY OF THE YEAR, YEAR C   18TH SUNDAY OF THE YEAR, YEAR C

*See 5th Sunday of the Year, Year C, p.164.*   *See 3rd Sunday of Lent, Year A, p.36.*

## 19TH SUNDAY OF THE YEAR, YEAR C

*See 5th Sunday of Easter, Year A, p.58, and Trinity Sunday, Year B, p.122.*

## 20TH SUNDAY OF THE YEAR, YEAR C

1st SETTING                    PAUL INWOOD

Response

Lord, Lord, come to my aid, come to my aid.

Psalm 39

1. I waited, I waited for the Lord and he stooped down to me; he heard my cry. R.

2. He drew me from the dead-ly pit, from the mi - ry clay. He set my feet up-on a rock and made my foot - steps firm. R. 3. He put a new song in my mouth, praise of our God. Man - y shall see and fear and shall trust in the Lord. R.

4. As for me, wretched and poor, the Lord thinks of me. You are my res - cu - er, my

help,  O  God,  do  not  de - lay.  ℞.

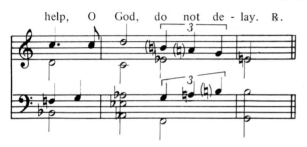

**2nd SETTING**

**Response**          GEOFFREY BOULTON SMITH

Lord,          come  to my    aid.

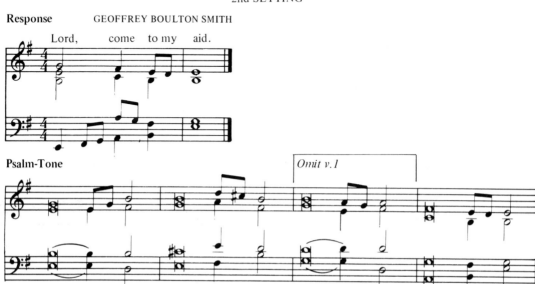

**Psalm-Tone**                    *Omit v.1*

**Ps 39**

1.  I waited, I waited | for the | Lord
    and he stooped | down to | me;
    he | heard my | cry.  ℞.

2.  He drew me from the | deadly | pit,
    from the | miry | clay.
    He set my feet up|on a | rock
    and made my | footsteps | firm.  ℞.

3.  He put a new song in|to my | mouth,
    praise | of our | God.
    Many shall | see and | fear
    and shall trust | in the | Lord.  ℞.

4.  As for me, wret|ched and | poor,
    the Lord | thinks of | me.
    You are my rescu|er, my | help,
    O God, do | not de|lay.  ℞.

# 21ST SUNDAY OF THE YEAR, YEAR C

*See 9th Sunday of the Year, Year C, p.167*

# 22ND SUNDAY OF THE YEAR, YEAR C

**Response**                                        MOUNT ST BERNARD

In  your  good - ness,  O  God,  you pre - pared_ a  home_ for  the  poor.

**Psalm-Tone**

**Ps 67**

1. The just shall rejoice at the presence | of | God,
   they shall exult and | dance for | joy.
   O sing to the Lord, make music to | his | name;
   rejoice in the Lord, exult | at his | presence. ℟.

2. Father of the orphan, defender of | the | widow,
   such is God in his | holy | place.
   God gives the lonely a home | to | live in;
   he leads the prisoners forth | into | freedom. ℟.

3. You poured down, O God, a | generous | rain;
   when your people were starved you gave | them new | life.
   It was there that your people found | a | home,
   prepared in your goodness, O God, | for the | poor. ℟.

## 23RD SUNDAY OF THE YEAR, YEAR C

**Response**                    1st SETTING                    LAURENCE BEVENOT

O Lord, you have been our re - fuge from one ge - ne - ra - tion to the next.

**Psalm-Tone**

**Ps 89**

1. You turn men back | into | dust
   and say: 'Go back | sons of | men.'
   To your eyes a thousand years are like yesterday, | come and | gone,
   no more than a watch | in the | night. ℟.

2. You sweep men away | like a | dream,
   like grass which springs up | in the | morning.
   In the morning it springs | up and | flowers:
   by evening it wi|thers and | fades. ℟.

3. Make us know the shortness | of our | life
   that we may gain wis|dom of | heart.
   Lord, relent! Is your an|ger for | ever?
   Show pity | to your | servants. ℟.

4. In the morning, fill us | with your | love;
   we shall exult and rejoice | all our | days.
   Let the favour of the Lord | be up|on us:
   give success to the work | of our | hands. ℟.

## 24TH SUNDAY OF THE YEAR, YEAR C
*See 1st Sunday of Lent, Year A, p.32.*

## 25TH SUNDAY OF THE YEAR, YEAR C

**Response**                                                BILL TAMBLYN

**Psalm-Tone**                                            JOSEPH GELINEAU

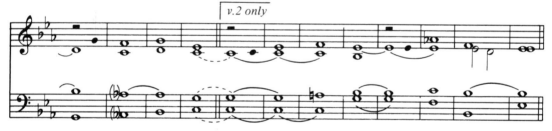

**Ps 112**

1. Alleluia! Práise, O sérvants of the Lórd,
   práise the náme of the Lórd!
   May the náme of the Lórd be bléssed
   both nów and for évermóre! ℟.

2. Hígh above all nátions is the Lórd,
   abóve the héavens his glóry.
   Whó is like the Lórd, our Gód,
   who has rísen on hígh to his thróne
   yet stóops from the héights to look dówn,
   to look dówn upon héaven and éarth? ℟.

3. From the dúst he lífts up the lówly,
   from the dúngheap he ráises the póor
   to sét him in the cómpany of prínces,
   yés, with the prínces of his péople. ℟.

## 26TH SUNDAY OF THE YEAR, YEAR C
*See 23rd Sunday of the Year, Year B, p.139.*

## 27TH SUNDAY OF THE YEAR, YEAR C
*See 3rd Sunday of Lent, Year A, p.36.*

## 28TH SUNDAY OF THE YEAR, YEAR C
*See Christmas Day, p.20, and 6th Sunday of Easter, Year B, p.120.*

## 29TH SUNDAY OF THE YEAR, YEAR C

PAUL INWOOD

Response

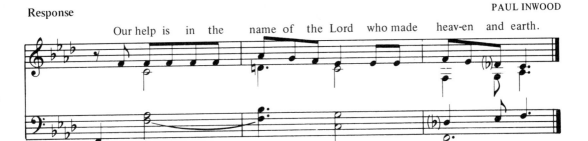

Our help is in the name of the Lord who made heav-en and earth.

Psalm-Tone

Ps 120

1.  I lift up my eyes to the | mountains:
    from where shall come my | help?
    My help shall | come from the | Lord
    who made heaven | and | earth.  ℟.

2.  May he never allow you to | stumble!
    Let him sleep not, your | guard.
    No, he | sleeps not nor | slumbers,
    Is|rael's | guard.  ℟.

3.  The Lord is your guard and your | shade;
    at your right side he | stands.
    By day the | sun shall not | smite you
    nor the moon in | the | night.  ℟.

4.  The Lord will guard you from | evil,
    he will guard your | soul.
    The Lord will guard your | going and | coming
    both now and | for | ever.  ℟.

# 30TH SUNDAY OF THE YEAR, YEAR C

**Response**                                      GEOFFREY BOULTON SMITH

**Psalm-Tone**                                    JOSEPH GELINEAU

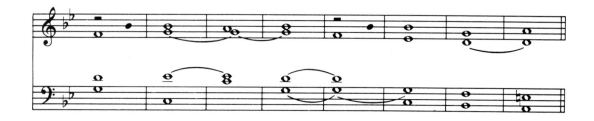

**Ps 33**

1. I will bléss the Lórd at áll times,
   his práise álways on my líps;
   in the Lórd my sóul shall make its bóast.
   The húmble shall héar and be glád.   ℞.

2. The Lórd turns his fáce against the wícked
   to destróy their remémbrance from the éarth.
   The júst cáll and the Lórd hears
   and réscues them in áll their distréss.   ℞.

3. The Lord is clóse to the bróken-héarted;
   those whose spírit is crúshed he will sáve.
   The Lord ránsoms the sóuls of his sérvants.
   Those who híde in him shall nót be condémned.   ℞.

# 31ST SUNDAY OF THE YEAR, YEAR C
*See 14th Sunday of the Year, Year A, p.82.*

# 32ND SUNDAY OF THE YEAR, YEAR C

SEBASTIAN WOLFF

**Response**

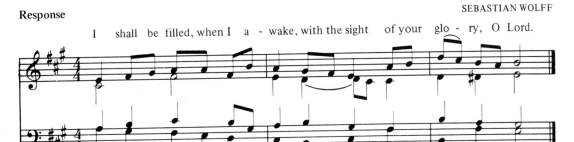

I shall be filled, when I a - wake, with the sight of your glo - ry, O Lord.

**Psalm-Tone**

**Ps 16**

1.  Lord, hear a cause | that is | just,
    pay heed | to my | cry.
    Turn your ear | to my | prayer:
    no deceit is | on my | lips.  R̩.

2.  I kept my feet firmly | in your | paths;
    there was no faltering | in my | steps.
    I am here and I call, you will hear | me, O | God.
    Turn your ear to me; | hear my | words.  R̩.

3.  Hide me in the shadow | of your | wings.
    As for me, in my justice I shall | see your | face
    and be filled, when | I a|wake,
    with the sight | of your | glory.  R̩.

# 33RD SUNDAY OF THE YEAR, YEAR C

**Response**

PAUL JOHNSTONE

The Lord comes, comes to rule the peo - ples with fair - ness,

**Psalm 97**

1. Sing psalms to the Lord with the harp with the sound of
2. Let the sea _ and all with-in it thun - der; the _ world, and all its
3. For the Lord comes, comes to rule the earth. _ He will rule the world with

1. mu - sic. With [ ] trum-pets and the _
2. peo-ples. Let the ri - vers _ clap their hands and the hills ring _
3. jus-tice [

*v.2 only*

*vv. 1 & 2 only*

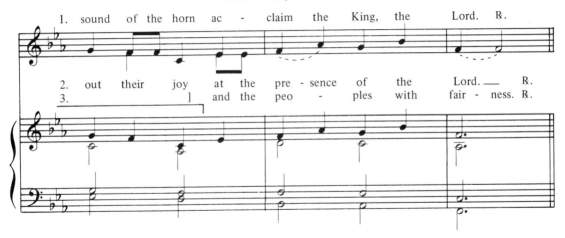

1. sound of the horn ac - claim the King, the Lord. ℞.

2. out their joy at the pre - sence of the Lord. ___ ℞.
3. ] and the peo - ples with fair - ness. ℞.

2nd SETTING

**Response**                                                    GEOFFREY BOULTON SMITH

The Lord comes to rule the peo - ples with fair - ness.

**Psalm-Tone**

*v.2 only*     *vv.1 & 2 only*

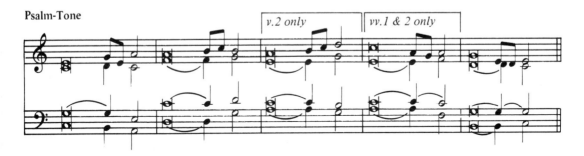

**Ps 97**

1. Sing psalms to the Lord | with the | harp
   with the | sound of | music.
   With trumpets and the sound | of the | horn
   acclaim the | King, the | Lord.   ℞.

2. Let the sea and all with|in it | thunder;
   the world, and | all its | peoples.
   Let the rivers | clap their | hands
   and the hills ring | out their | joy
   at the presence | of the | Lord.   ℞.

3. For the Lord comes, comes to | rule the | earth.
   He will rule the | world with | justice
   and the peo|ples with | fairness.   ℞.

## LAST SUNDAY OF THE YEAR, YEAR C
### Solemnity of Christ the King
*See 1st Sunday of Advent, Year A, p.13.*

## DEDICATION OF A CHURCH   I

*See 1st Sunday of Advent, Year A, p.13.*

### DEDICATION OF A CHURCH   II

**Response**                                        GEOFFREY BOULTON SMITH

**Psalm-Tone**

Ps 83

1.  My soul is | longing and | yearning,
    is yearning for the | courts of the | Lord.
    My heart and my soul ring | out their | joy
    to God, the | living | God.   R.

2.  The sparrow her|self·finds a | home
    and the swallow a | nest for her | brood;
    she lays her young | by your | altars,
    Lord of hosts, my king | and my | God.   R.

3.  They are happy, who | dwell in your | house,
    for ever | singing your | praise.
    They are happy, whose strength | is in | you,
    they walk with ever|growing | strength.   R.

4.  One day | within your | courts
    is better than a | thousand else|where.
    The threshold of the | house of | God
    I prefer to the dwellings | of the | wicked.   R.

# GOSPEL ACCLAMATIONS
## and
## ALLELUIA VERSES

*With the exception of the first few settings, which have been written for specific seasons of the Church's Year, nearly all the settings have been provided with single tones to which most verse-texts may be fitted.*

## CHRISTMAS MIDNIGHT and CHRISTMAS DAY

JAMES WALSH

M'night: I bring you good news, good news of great joy: to-day a sa - viour
Day: A hal - lowed day has dawned on us. ___ Come, you nations,

**(Choir divisi)**

M: has been born, a sa-viour has been born_ to us, he is Christ the
D: wor-ship the Lord,_ for to-day a great light has shone, for to-day a

M: Lord, he is Christ the Lord,_ Christ the Lord.
D: great light has shone, shone down up-on_ the earth.

**SEASON OF LENT**

JAMES WALSH

Praise_ to you, O Christ, king of e-ter-nal glo-ry!
*or:* Glo-ry to you, O Christ, you are the Word of God!_

*or:* Glo-ry and praise to you, O Christ; glo-ry and praise to you, O Christ!

**Tone**

## SEASON OF LENT

CHRISTOPHER WALKER

Praise and ho-nour to you, Lord Je - sus!

**Tone**

## PALM SUNDAY/GOOD FRIDAY

*To be sung unaccompanied. The setting consists of two alternated melodic germs.*

PAUL INWOOD

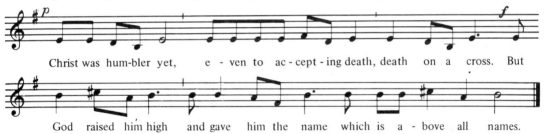

Christ was hum-bler yet, e - ven to ac-cept-ing death, death on a cross. But

God raised him high and gave him the name which is a - bove all names.

*For Maundy Thursday, see the psalm-setting for this day, p.46.*

## EASTER VIGIL and EASTERTIDE

ADAPTED FROM PLAINCHANT

Al - le - lu - ia, al - le - lu - ia, al le - - lu - ia!_____

**Tone**

# EASTER SUNDAY and EASTERTIDE
## also for general use

ADAPTED FROM PLAINCHANT

## EASTER SUNDAY and EASTERTIDE

GEOFFREY BOULTON SMITH

Al-le-lu - ia, Al-le-lu - ia,

Al-le-lu - ia! Christ, our passover, has been sacrificed; let us celebrate the

feast, then, in the Lord.

*Repeat ALLELUIA*

**Alternative Simple Tone**
**for use during Easter season**

## GENERAL 1

A. GREGORY MURRAY

Al - le - lu - ia, al - le - lu - ia, al - le - lu - ia!

Tone

## GENERAL 2

LAURENCE BÉVENOT

Al - le - lu - ia, al - le - lu - ia, al - le - lu - ia!

Tone

## GENERAL 3

LAURENCE BÉVENOT

**Tone**

## GENERAL 4

LAURENCE BÉVENOT

## GENERAL 5

GEOFFREY BOULTON SMITH

The opening Alleluia should be sung by choir or cantor, and repeated by all. In the final Alleluia the people sing the lower line. Choir sopranos may add the upper part, or the choir may divide ST (top part) and AB (bottom part). If the descant is not sung, repeat the opening Alleluia instead.

## GENERAL 6

GEOFFREY BOULTON SMITH

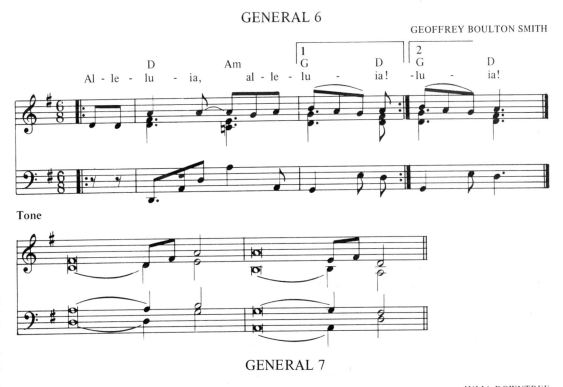

## GENERAL 7

JULIA ROWNTREE

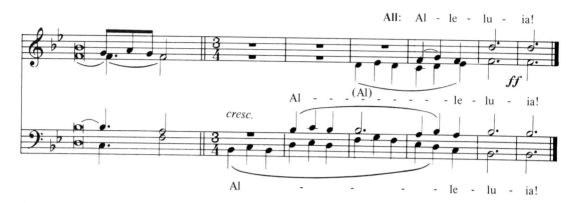

## GENERAL 8

*The Alleluia may be sung as a 4-part round.*
*Lively*

MICHAEL COY

**Tone**

## GENERAL 9

TONY BARR

*The final Alleluia may be sung as a 3-part round*

**Tone**

Al - le - lu - ia,— al - le - lu - ia!

## GENERAL 10

CHRISTOPHER WALKER

Al - le - lu - ia, al - le - lu - ia, al - le - lu - ia!

**Tone**

## *PREMANANDA ALLELUIA

*A Bengali word meaning 'Love-joy'

CHRISTOPHER WALKER

**People may move to other lines at will.

*It is suggested that, after the basic Alleluia is established, a new line should be added every four Alleluias.
Percussion ad lib., but a strong first beat of the bar is essential. Melody-instruments double the voices.
Start softly and grow gradually, reaching a climax as the Gospel Procession reaches the ambo.*

# INDEX OF PSALMS

*Page references indicate pages on which settings of these psalms begin*

# INDEX OF COMPOSERS

*With acknowledgements to *Tones for the Office* published 1978 by Parish Music, Cathedral Precinct, Liverpool, where some of these first appeared.